THE SECRET OF GOOD HEALTH - OLIVE OIL

Translation: **Maria Bitsakaki-Psilaki**
Melanie Godwin

Photographs: Nikos Psilakis

Layout: Nikos Dretakis

Printing: TYPOKRETA, Heraklion
Bookbinding: Z. Mouthatsakis, Skoteino, Heraklion

ISBN: 960-7448-32-4

Lophos Semeli
715 00 Heraklion
Crete, Greece
Tel. & Fax: 0030 810 261920
E-mail: npsilakis@otenet.gr

www.karmanor.gr

Nikos & Maria
Psilakis

The secret of good health
Olive Oil

Advice on its correct use

With 130 recipes

KARMANOR
Under the Auspices
of the Greek Academy of Taste

CON

ENTS

THE OLIVE TREE AND ITS OIL IN PREHISTORIC TIMES

For thousands of years now, the inhabitants of the Mediterranean countries have cultivated the olive tree and used its products for their daily needs. The edible olives and oil were used in their food, the leaves and the oil had therapeutic powers or were used as incense and the oil was also used as an offering to the gods.

Greeks based their diet on olive products for thousands of years. On Crete, in the south of the Peloponnese, on the islands of the Aegean and in many other areas, olive oil was almost exclusively used as the fat content in food. This is why the olive tree is such a beloved tree, blessed by God himself and seen as holy, in the eyes of Greek folklore tradition.

The olive tree has its origins in the Mediterranean and greatly influenced the formation of a civilization in a place where some of the earliest human civilizations were developed. Charming old and newer legends, along with ancient customs which still survive, prove without doubt the connection of the olive tree with both ancient and later forms of worship. The development of a civilization can be seen

Jars were for thousands of years the commonest containers for storing olive oil (Minoan jar, 2nd millennium B.C.)

through the people's diet. The identity of an area is shaped by the goods that are produced there. Wheat, wine and olive oil are the main products of Greece. All three are blessed and they have been used as a part of holy worship for thousands of years.

Fresco from the palace of Cnossos depicting "the sacred grove" (17th-16th c. B.C.).

The cultivation of grain crops shows the evolution of society, a system whereby a farmer stored food that was collected, in order to attain

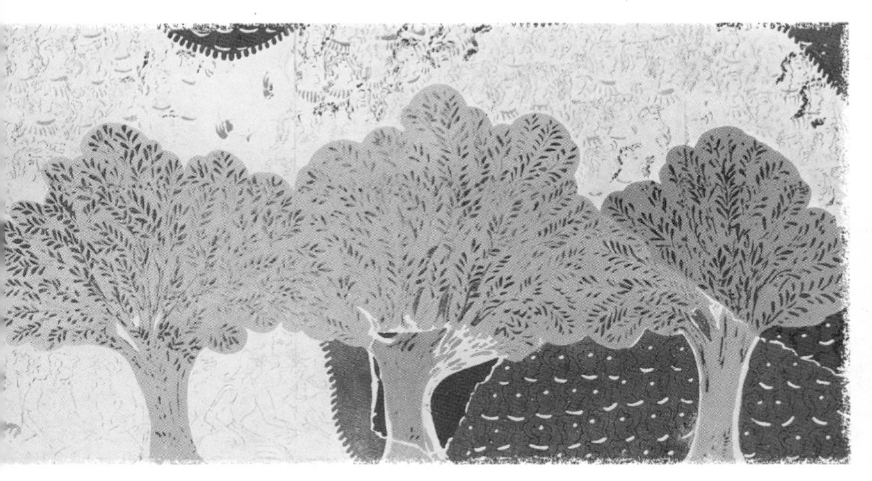

an established standard of living. The pressing of olives and the extraction of olive oil came much later, when mankind had developed a higher form of civilization which was characterized by the development of technology... The machinery that was invented for use in the processing of food products are maybe the first ones invented by the human mind.

THE OLIVE TREE - 60,000 YEARS OLD

But when did the olive tree appear? The tree, indigenous to the Mediterranean area, seems to have been around for thousands of years. A fossilized leaf of the *olea noti* family has been found at Kyme on Euboea, while evidence which proves the scattered spreading out of the tree has been found in Provence in

France and in the countries of Northern Africa. This extremely old piece of evidence fills you with awe for the antiquity of this tree. It originates from the islands of the Aegean, Santorini and Nisyros, where professor Evangelos Velitzelos discovered fossilized olive tree leaves aged fifty to sixty thousands years old! Experts on Palaeobotany believe that what was discovered were leaves of cultivated olive trees.

Fossilized olive leaves. They have been found by prof. E. Velitzelos on the Aegean islands.

EDIBLE OLIVES - 3500 YEARS OLD!

An impressive archaeological discovery bears witness to the relationship between the edible olive in cooking and in worship. Archaeologists who carried out excavations on Crete, in the area of Zakros on the east side of the island, have uncovered olives aged 3500 years!

The olives which were found in an ancient well at Zakros, Crete, after 3,500 years!

These olives looked fresh since they had retained their skins. The city had been destroyed due to an earthquake before 3500 years. Archaeologists have given a logical reason for this finding. A short while before the disastrous earthquake which finally brought down the palace, during the pre-earthquake tremors that had already started (a warning of the forthcoming disaster), offerings were made to the gods in the form of bowls filled with edible olives. It was judged that the most suitable place for this offering was a well. The people probably believed that by placing the offerings in the well, they would be closer to the powers of the Underworld, the same ones that could cause such strong earth tremors. When archaeologists uncovered the well, a bowl full of olives was found and they, too, had kept their skins after so many years! A few minutes after their discovery the olives disintegrated but, thankfully, the archaeologists managed to take

Gold amulets in the shape of olive tree leaves from Mochlos.

pictures of them. *"I was down in the well and we were looking around the water. Suddenly my hand fell on a bowl which contained both dry and slimy things. We took the bowl out and, to our joy, saw that there were olives in it, not very big but shiny ones".* Ancient people used to place their offerings to the gods of the Underworld in holes or hollows in the earth.

Representation of an olive tree on a fresco at Cnossos.

The Minoan goddess of snakes. She was succeeded by Athena, the goddess who was associated with the olive tree.

Ideograms symbolizing olive oil, the olive tree and olive fruit in Linear B script, around 1400 B.C

OLIVES AND OLIVE OIL IN IDEOGRAMS

Around 2000 B.C. people used symbols (ideograms) for olive trees and olive oil. This ancient type of writing is known as Linear A. In the still unpublished work by Menas Tzikritzis, it is claimed that on offering tables from southern Crete dated back to 18th century B.C., ideograms of olive trees and olive oil can be read next to the name Athena, the Greek goddess who is believed to have first planted the olive tree. The same ideogram or symbol can still be seen after the destruction of the Minoan civilization. Linear A tablets that were found in Archanes show ideograms which describe different types of food. Among those are ideograms

Tablets with ideograms referring to the olive oil.

depicting olive trees, olive oil, wheat and wine.

People in ancient times continued to write on clay tablets after the fall of the Minoan civilization.

Fragment from a fresco at Cnossos depicting an olive tree.

The tablets written after 1450 B.C. were different from their predecessors. Following the Second World War, an ingenious English cryptologist, Michael Ventris, managed to decipher them. In this way, he offered a valuable gift to the world, as it shed light on life two thousand years before Christ. There are many points of evidence which indicate both olive trees and olive oil. People of that time not only cultivated olive trees but also scented their oil with herbs. They produced aromatic oil and this was offered along with the non-scented oil to the gods. On one of the tablets there is even an olive shown as a form of food.

The ideograms with which the Minoans and later the Mycenaeans declared their olive oil in a shorthand type are quite impressive. People at Cnossos used a symbol very similar to the olive tree itself. The ideogram which represents the olive looks like an olive tree flower and a special ideogram was used for the olive oil.

HOMERIC TIMES

The olive tree seems to have had its own special role in daily life in Homeric times. Homer, the famous poet of ancient Greece, left us with two enormously important poems with regards to human civilization, in which there is interesting information about the olive tree and its oil. It is said in the poems that in the gardens of Alkinoos, the king of the Phaeakae, there were olive trees along with other trees which had edible fruits. It is also stated that olive wood was used in

Mycenae. Installations for the preparation of scented oil have been found in this ancient city. Right: An ages-old olive tree.

the making of furniture. Odysseus, the hero who roamed the seas for ten years, built his bed from olive wood.

Edible olives and scented oil were well known in Homeric times. The specially prepared oil was used in caring for the body as well as the bodies of the dead. Even Aphrodite, the beautiful goddess of love, used rose-scented oil when she anointed Hector's dead body, one of the leading characters in the Trojan war.

Olive harvesting in ancient times.

THE OLIVE TREE AND ITS OIL IN THE CLASSICAL PERIOD

Information about the olive tree and its oil has become more readily available as the years went by. As society developed, the olive tree became more valuable. Moreover, measures were taken to protect these trees. It is known that the olive tree was cultivated and protected by particular laws in Athens. In 5th century B.C., the Athenians introduced special measures to protect olive trees while at the same time, there were sacred trees which were believed to have descended from the very same olive tree that Athena, the goddess of wisdom, had planted on the holy

rock of the Acropolis. This was believed to have been the first olive tree to have been planted in the world! Zeus, the great god of the Greeks, was the protector of these holy trees. These trees were, at the beginning, planted at Academia, in the "sacred grove", but later they were cultivated in various other areas in Attica.

"Everyone has to plant an olive tree..."

In an ancient Cretan town known as Dreros, which was to be found close by to today's Aghios Nikolaos, an ancient inscription has been discovered which includes a grave oath. This oath obliges every young man to plant at least one olive tree and to look after it until it has fully grown. This custom seems to have been the practice in other towns, too. It is highly possible that this was the main ritual in an initiation into a social group.

THE ROMAN AND BYZANTINE PERIODS

During Roman times, olive oil became much more widely known in many areas. The enormous Roman Empire often undertook measures to ensure that its citizens did not suffer from a shortage of olive oil. Not only the import to Rome but also its distribution was overseen. Trade developed rapidly and Roman ships transported large quantities of olive oil to areas where the olive tree was not cultivated or to places where a small production of oil did not meet the demands of the locals.

Carbonized olives from Pompei.

Meanwhile, the olive tree and its oil continued to play an important role in religion and worship. The Christian religion, originated in the Mediterranean and having therefore its roots in the long tradition of the area, very soon incorporated a lot

Olive harvesting in Byzantium. Detail from an illustrated Byzantine manuscript.

of ancient rituals which associated ancient worship with both the olive tree and the olive oil. The olive tree continued to be regarded as sacred, as was natural and as would be expected in religions which existed in the "olive zone', that is in the Mediterranean area... Let us not forget the olive mountain, the place where Jesus Christ himself went to pray.

Olive harvesting on Lesbos. A picture by the popular painter Theophilus.

The cultivation of olive trees continued for many centuries to be one of the main forms of occupation for the inhabitants of Greece. With regards to the Byzantine period, we have many useful pieces of information, both direct and indirect, which have helped us to find out more about large-scale production of olive oil in certain areas, such as the Peloponnese. After the fall of the Byzantine Empire in 1453 A.D., the olive became the symbol of survival for the inhabitants of many agricultural areas. Living under extremely difficult conditions, these people found a relatively easy product which could be put to many uses and so ensured their survival. Information which has been saved bears witness to the fact that people used olive oil in cooking on a regular basis. Recipes from the Byzantine and Post Byzantine period have even been discovered. Olive oil does not seem to have been used so systematically for human consumption in the other Mediterranean countries at that time.

During the Turkish occupation the olive trade was the cause of dynamic economic development in many areas. This continued with the appearance of soap industry. In 18th century olive oil was exported to the European markets as a product to be used in soap production and not in the kitchen. The largest amount of olive oil was exported to Marseilles, which had become an important center of soap industry.

THE USE OF OLIVE OIL FOR LIGHTING

Since prehistoric times olive oil has been used for the lighting of houses and public buildings. The use of olive oil as lighting material has created a range of symbols in that olive oil is seen as a source of light!

In evening ceremonies which required lighting, the role of olive oil was sacred, as it still is in today's worship.

According to Herodotus (5th century B.C.) there was a special celebration in Egypt which was known as "lychnokajia" (lighting of the lamps). All people

Olive oil is the most ancient source of lighting. An oil lamp which was in use up until the middle of 20th century.

lit their lamps and it was a spectacular event.

In Byzantine times, olive oil was essential for the "lychnokajia" in the monasteries and the churches.

Up until the first few decades of this century, the farming population of Greece had olive oil as their basic fuel for lighting.

A bronze oil lamp from the town of Archanes, dated back to the Roman period.

THE OLIVE AND ITS OIL IN WORSHIP

Tree culture. The growth of the olive tree and its symbolism in eternal life

The olive tree impressed prehistoric man because it lived for hundreds of years and almost never dried out! New shoots grew in the dried trunks and so the plant was reborn. In the prehistoric religions of the Eastern Mediterranean, man worshipped an immortal couple, a goddess who is today known as the "Great Mother" and a young god who died and was reborn every year, along with the growth of plants. This brought about the creation of a religious tradition of respect towards nature. Evidence from Neolithic Crete has led us to the conclusion that man worshipped certain trees. They acted out dances of worship under these trees and touched them as maybe they wished to draw strength from them. Some of these trees seem to have been olive trees. The first piece of evidence regarding the special role which the olive tree played in worship can be seen on the sarcophagus at Aghia Triatha which was found in Messara on Crete. The tree can be recognized in the sacred grove, behind the altar. In ancient Athens (around 5th century B.C. or even earlier) an olive tree was worshipped which was to be found on the rock of the Acropolis. It is said that it was planted by the bright ancient goddess Athena, who was the beloved daughter of Zeus and herself the goddess of wisdom. The custom of worshipping sacred trees continued for thousands of years in the Greek region.

Representation of a sacred tree of worship on a Minoan ring from Archanes.

A sacred olive tree next to the altar. A religious representation on the sarcophagus of Aghia Triada (1500-1400 B.C.).

Right: The olive tree has "embraced" the ancient column (Gortyn, Crete).

THE OLIVE TREE AND ITS OIL IN THE CHRISTIAN RELIGION AND THE WORSHIP CUSTOMS

The olive tree and its oil accompany man from his birth till his death! In Cyprus, in older years, the newborn infant was given to drink water from upon an olive leaf, so that he would never feel dry in his life, just like the olive tree, which can survive under the toughest climate conditions. In certain areas on Crete, there is still the custom to put three olive branches into

"Olive oil seal" in the sacrament of baptism.

the grave! In the Christian faith olive oil is transformed into cure for both the body and the soul! Moreover, it is the way in which the grace of God is transferred and "seals" the faithful Christians! The significant role of this blessed liquid is visible in the baptism ceremony. The priest anoints the person to be baptized with purifying olive oil, which transmits the divine benediction. This is why there is a bottle with olive oil next to the font during the baptism ceremony! The olive oil is not used only in the sacrament of the baptism. The ceremony of the Holy Unction takes place in the Orthodox churches every Holy Wednesday. The same sacrament can also take place in sick people's houses... The priest anoints the face of the faithful with olive oil in the form of crosses, thus transferring the God's grace.

Left: Olive oil, wheat and wine in the Sacrament of Holy Unction.

OLIVE O

Soap was known in antiquity (it is mentioned by Galenus, a physician in the Roman times), however it was used more as a medicine. In older times it was prepared with ash (because of its potassium carbonate content), which was added to the olive oil. After 1790, when Nicolas Leblanc proceeded to the industrial production of soap, its use increased enormously.

Soap has the property to remove dirt from both the body and the clothes, when diluted in water. Soap made from olive oil is usually either green or white in colour, it is pure and friendly to the man's skin and provides hydration without irritating it. It is not toxic and is recommended for the cleaning of both the body and the clothes.

THE PERFECT CLEANING PRODUCT

Soap is regarded today, even after the tremendous expansion of synthetic detergents, as the perfect cleaning product. This is due to the fact that it is not toxic, acts effectively when used with soft water and doesn't pollute the environment.

The natural green soap is produced from residue oil of high acidity while the white soap is produced from pure olive oil.

PREPARATION OF OLIVE OIL SOAP

Soap is the result of the reaction between the esters contained in olive oil and other fatty substances and one basis (NaOH – caustic soda or KOH - caustic potassium). In the traditional soap manufacture olive oil (generally residue oil of high acidity, over 25 degrees) is put in cauldrons where a solution of caustic soda and water is added. The mixture is heated on low temperature and the soap production process starts... Heating is continued for about four hours and then extra

soda solution is added. Stirring is going on until a homogeneous soap mass is formed. Afterwards the remaining soda is removed with the addition of a certain amount of table salt: The waste waters, containing various impurities and glycerin, are concentrated at the bottom of the cauldron and are discarded while soap remains and floats on the surface. The soap mass is heated again until it obtains the desirable appearance. Next it is poured into moulds, which are left in an airy place to dry. Finally the soap blocks are stamped and are sold in the market. The whole production procedure usually takes four days.

(Information obtained from Mr Man. Griniezakis, head soap technician of the Peza Cooperative).

SOAP PREPARATION AT HOME

In the past, Greek housewives used to produce the soap they needed at home with olive oil of high acidity, over 20°, usually with the oil left from the frying of foods. A solution of about 270 grams of caustic soda in 600 ml water was added to about two litres of olive oil. The mixture was heated on a temperature of 40 degrees Celsius along with constant stirring, for about 15 minutes.

When the procedure was completed, the mixture was spread on a wooden surface brushed with a little olive oil and was left to dry in an airy place for 36 hours or longer. Then it was cut into square blocks with a knife. Others poured it into moulds so that it took the desirable shape. The disadvantage of this soap is that it contains glycerin (in professional soap manufacture and industry it is removed with the addition of table salt) and is not considered to be of high quality. However, we ourselves could experiment...

(Information obtained from Mr N. Kehagiadakis, a descendant of a soap producing family on Crete).

OLIVE OIL AS FOOD

"Olive oil in Greece takes the place butter has in the English diet"
(Antony Andrews, "Ancient Greek Society")

Olive oil had been essential for lighting as well as a basic dietary requirement since prehistoric times. Its uses in cooking were extended during the classical period. Complicated forms of cooking were concocted in order to meet the demand for unusual ideas. Archestratus has informed us about some rather interesting recipes using fish; olive oil was often used with cheese and vegetables. Two-banded bream for example, a well known tasty fish, was cooked with cheese and olive oil. Glaucus (a kind of sea bass) was boiled in water with spices and olive oil. Then the fish was put in brine. This is all according to the recipe which was saved by Oreibasius, a famous doctor in the Byzantine times.

Olive oil was essential in cooking cereal crops, vegetables and pulses, as it still is in

traditional Greek cuisine, especially in the areas where olive trees are abundant.

Olive oil which was to be used for cooking purposes was always of a very high standard, obviously depending on the conditions of production in every area. Farmers were used to consuming the olive oil without it being cooked, which is not such an unusual occurrence even today, either by pouring the

oil on a traditional Greek dried rusk or by flavouring boiled greens and other kinds of salad. The amounts of uncooked oil that were consumed were not small.

Olive oil was not only used for basic cooking, but also for making sweets. Athenaeus, a great writer who recorded a lot of information about food and diet in the Roman era, mentions an ancient Cretan sweet which was called "glycinas". It was made "*with sweet wine and olive oil*".

Many sweets in ancient times and even today's traditional ones rely on olive oil.

Tripod Minoan pot. Recent analyses proved that ancient people cooked food in them using olive oil even before 2000 B.C.

OLIVE OIL IN THE CRETAN DIET. THE STUDY OF THE SEVEN COUNTRIES

"Olives and olive oil play an important role in the Cretan diet. A foreign visitor has the impression that Cretan food literally floats in olive oil"

(Experimental research by the Rockefeller Foundation, 1948).

"They even cook pork in olive oil"

(M. Chourmouzis - Vyzantius, 1842)

Today, the Cretan diet is believed to be the best example of a Mediterranean diet and researchers have discovered that the Cretans have the lowest rate of heart diseases and cancer. The Cretans' good health is thought to be due to their diet. The largest role in the Cretan diet is played by olive oil.

The surprise felt by travellers when they saw Cretans or inhabitants from other large olive growing areas consuming oil unsparingly is quite justified. These habits were completely different from their own dietary ideas. Animal fat is the norm in the urban communities of central Europe.

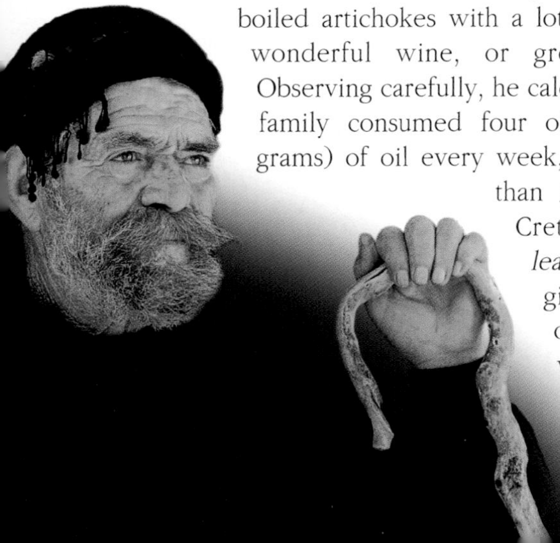

The English traveller Robert Pashley, who toured Crete shortly after the revolution of 1821 (the rebellion which brought about freedom for only one part of Greece), has provided us with important pictures of everyday life, which in themselves prove the leading role of olive oil in the diet of the inhabitants. In the villages he was often offered boiled artichokes with a lot of olive oil, eggs and wonderful wine, or greens with olive oil. Observing carefully, he calculated that each Cretan family consumed four okades (1 oka = 1280 grams) of oil every week, in other words, more than 350 litres a year! The Cretans, he says, "*are learned in olive oil*". They give it to their children on bread, they use it with all greens, even with meat and fish. "It

is the only thing that they are liberal with", he notes!

The extreme consumption of olive oil made a lasting impression on all visitors to the olive producing areas of Greece during the 19th century.

M. Chourmouzis – Vyzantius fought against the Turkish occupation of Crete in the years 1828-1829 and subsequently lived on the island for six years in total. He keenly observed the habits of the local population. The extensive use of olive oil was what impressed him most.

He says that the Cretans *"eat vegetables as well as different types of tasty wild greens which, along with barley bread, are very good for them"*.

He says that the inhabitants of the island overused olive oil and notes with surprise, *"they cook even pork in olive oil"*.

The observations made by Chourmouzis-Vyzantius had previously been made by many others who had visited the oil

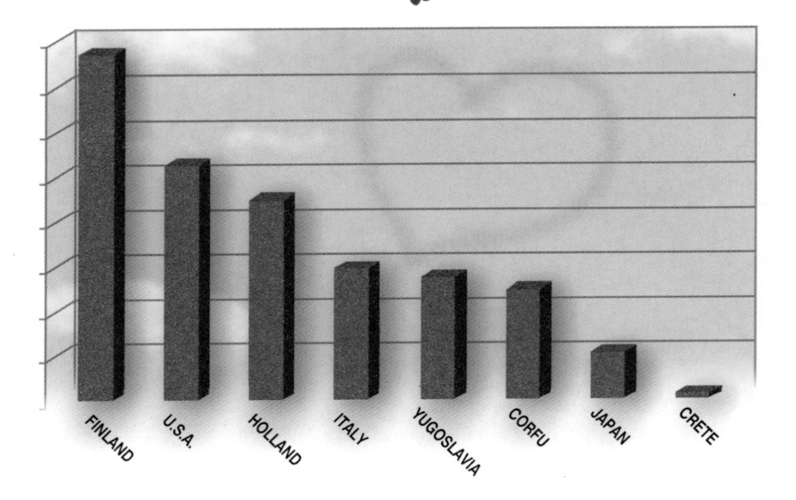

DEATHS FROM CORONARY DISEASE PER 100,000 INHABITANTS (Study of the Seven Countries)

producing areas of Greece, such as Pouqueville and Bartholdy.

Even in Constantinople, where Chourmouzis - Vyzantius gained his experiences, the cuisine had different styles.

The study of the Seven Countries which was organized by Anzel Keys towards the end of the 1950s greatly surprised the international scientific community.

The Cretans, whose food floated in oil, were found to have the best health in the world. Cancerous diseases were rare, in fact much less frequent than all the areas studied and perhaps in all the world, and cardiovascular diseases (a real threat for inhabitants in the north), were almost unknown on Crete. Keys himself bore witness to the fact that the Cretans consumed large amounts of olive oil: *"You should see how much olive oil they use"!*

A few years earlier on Crete, an experimental survey was carried out on the society and economy of the island by the American Rockefeller Foundation (L. G. Allbaugh - G. Soule). The chapter about diet contains a lot of information about the island.

Let us look at one observation in the study:

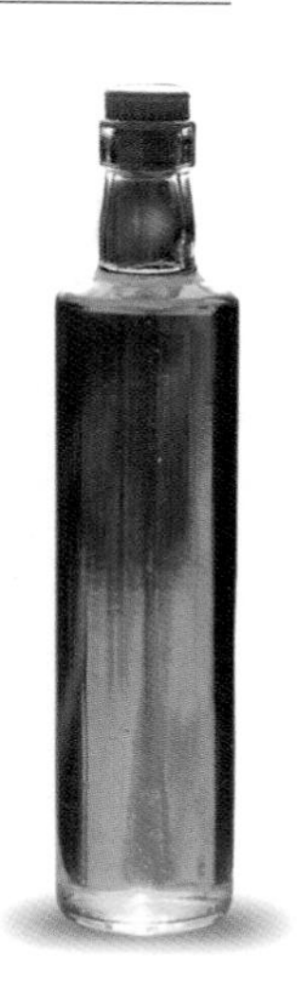

"Olives and olive oil make up a large part of the Cretan diet. A foreign visitor has the impression that Cretan food floats in oil. This product is unsparingly used in cooking. It is essential for salads, soups and vegetables..."

In another part it states:

"The consumption of fat but, most importantly of all, olive oil is great.
This level of olive oil consumption is characteristic of the Cretan diet, in fact, much greater than anywhere else in Greece".

Any other form of fat would only occasionally be used on Crete.

THE CONSUMPTION OF OLIVE OIL IN THE CRETAN DIET

The study of the seven countries in the 1950s showed that the consumption of olive oil on Crete was extremely high in comparison to the other areas of the Mediterranean and especially in contrast to the northern countries. In reality, the consumption of fat by the Cretans, the other Mediterranean countries, Holland and the U.S.A. is shown as being 95, 60, 79 and 33 grams per person per day accordingly. On Crete and in the other Mediterranean countries the fat is almost entirely olive oil whereas in the U.S.A. it is other kinds of oils.

In Holland, butter and animal fats are the norm.

Similar studies by Eurostat, the statistics service of the European Union, showed that, in 1996, the consumption of olive oil was at a level of 31 litres annually per person on Crete, 25 litres in the other Mediterranean countries and only 185 grams per person per year in Germany!

These rates of consumption show 85 and 62 grams per person per day for the two population groups, further emphasizing an important stability in the use of olive oil, despite the great social and dietary changes which have taken place in all the Mediterranean countries in the last few decades.

THE OLIVE AND ITS OIL AS A MEDICINE

A writer in ancient times known as Aelianus (3rd century AD), claimed that olive oil and the olive tree flowers were medicines that could be used even on elephants so as to pull out arrows if hunters had succeeded in hitting them:

> *"When an elephant is injured by many arrow heads, it eats olive tree flowers or oil and then whatever has hurt it can be removed. It is at once again strong".*

It is well known that olive oil was believed to be a cure for all wounds and this knowledge continued in popular medicine for many centuries.

Bathing and rubbing with olive oil during the Olympic and other games in Greek ancient times.

Doctors in ancient times and in the Byzantine world mention an array of prescriptions which use olive oil as a basic ingredient. It was mainly used against fever by being rubbed onto the body of the person who had a temperature and also as a neurological medicine. Many doctors in ancient times recommended bathing in lukewarm olive oil for those who suffered from neuralgia. There are many ancient prescriptions which use olive oil as a basic ingredient. In general we could say that there were hardly any illnesses that could not be cured with olive oil.

A lit oil lamp hanging in front of Christ's icon.

It was used against poisoning, for oral health and in keeping teeth white, against stomach problems, dermatitis and leprosy which was a disease that continually appeared in the sub-tropical areas up until quite recently. The best oil for therapeutic reasons was the oil taken from the oil lamps of the icons.

Fr. Richard, who visited the island of Chios in 1650, wrote that the abbot of the New Monastery, gave out threads, which had been dipped in the oil of these lamps, to the faithful!

OLIVE OIL AS AN APHRODISIAC

"Eat olive oil and come at night eat butter and sleep tight"

Popular medicine used olive oil as an aphrodisiac. The saying repeated in many olive oil producing areas of Greece is *"eat olive oil and come at night"* and this echoes folklore ideas. On Crete, olive oil which had not been cooked was deemed to be a much more effective aphrodisiac, especially if the oil came from the wild varieties of olive trees. It was with this belief that many newly weds had to eat bread soaked in the first olive oil of the year. It was thought to be an elixir for conception in the south of Crete. A Thessalian saying judges the fat content of the oil and considers it to be an aphrodisiac (a belief that is held all over Greece) and that butter is a substance which weakens the sexual desire:

"Eat butter and sleep tight eat olive oil and come at night"

An athlete is rubbing his body with olive oil (representation on a crater from Attica, dating back to 500 B.C. and now exhibited in Berlin Museum).

SYMBOLIZATION
The tree of peace

The use of olive branches in a range of ancient rituals, such as in purification, shows clearly how the olive tree was a sign of goodness. The same tree was linked to light since the burning of olive oil was the leading source of light. This consolidation of ideas, which is almost the same in all Mediterranean civilizations, gave a specific position to the olive tree. The olive tree is the tree of hope in the Old Testament but also a tree - a message of mercy from God, that

A Syrian monk is holding an olive branch, the symbol of peace, and is trying to reach the besieged church of Nativity (April 2000). The picture has been published on the cover of the magazine «The Olive Tree and its Oil".

was brought to the arc by a dove to show that the flood had ended. Greek tradition looks upon this tree as the symbol of peace. Eirini (Peace) herself, the goddess who was the daughter of Zeus and Themis, is pictured with an olive branch in her hands. There was no better way or symbol of the end of a war than a branch from this tree. Messengers who were sent with a message of peace or to ask for a settlement, carried an olive branch in their hands. It was the unquestioned holy symbol which declared the intentions of those who decided to send it.

THE OLIVE AND ITS OIL IN ANCIENT MYTHOLOGY

ATHENA'S GIFT OF THE OLIVE TREE

The most well known ancient myth relating to the cultivation of the olive tree tells how Athena, the great goddess, gave the olive tree as a present. Some state that she first planted the tree on Crete and later in Athens whereas others believe that the wise goddess first planted this tree on the holy rock of the Acropolis.

It all started with the disagreement between Athena and Poseidon. Athena was the goddess of wisdom and Poseidon was the god of the sea. Both of them wanted to govern Athens, the most amazing Greek city in the classical period. Based on this, each immortal decided to offer an invaluable present. The winner of this unusual contest was to be the one who offered the most precious gift. The judges of these two gods were all the other immortals who did not take pleasure in watching this contest between the gods.

Ancient Athenian coins with olive branch wreaths and olive branches accordingly.

Poseidon, lord of the seas, appeared in the contest with his trident, the one which decided the fate of the seas. He lifted his trident and stabbed it into the side of the holy rock of the Acropolis. Salty water started to fall down the sides of the rock. It has been said that he opened a well with his trident on the rock of the Acropolis and that it was full of salty water. Poseidon believed that such a well in Attica would bring him victory.

Athena did not need to do anything too impressive. She bent down and planted an olive tree in the same spot. Others suggest that she did not plant it herself. She just stabbed her javelin into the earth and the tree immediately flourished. Its silver-green foliage impressed everyone.

That was it! The world had never seen such a tree. As people could not try cooked food or enjoy a lit night as there was no suitable fuel for the wicks, the gods judged that Athena's gift was of invaluable worth.

The holy tree of Athens has a story of its own in the city. In 480 B.C., when the Persians invaded and took the Acropolis, the holy tree of Athena was burned down, much to the great sadness of the Athenians who took it to be a very bad sign. This despair turned to joy the next morning when from the burnt remains of the tree, appeared a new bud. This young plant was the new holy tree of Athena's!

The goddess Athena is offering the precious gift of the olive tree to the city of Athens. Representation on a crater dating from around 400 B.C.

THE OLIVE TREE AND ALIRRHOTHIOS

The decision of the gods which sided with Athena in the battle over Athens, greatly angered Poseidon who, as ruler of the seas, never allowed Attica to have enough water. Not only was Poseidon upset by this decision but also his family. One of his sons, an offspring from his affair with the nymph Euryte, was called Alirrhothios.

Angered by the lack of respect shown to his father, Alirrhothios went up to the top of the holy rock of the Acropolis, took an axe and tried to chop down the one and only olive tree which Athena had planted. The axe slipped in his hands so that, instead of hitting the olive tree, it stuck him and cut off his head or his leg, but the result was his death.

The contest between Athena and Poseidon. Piece of work produced at Donatello's atelier, 15th c. (Source: Museo dell' Olivo, Imperia). Below: The Acropolis of Athens.

THE OLIVE TREE IN THE OLYMPIC GAMES

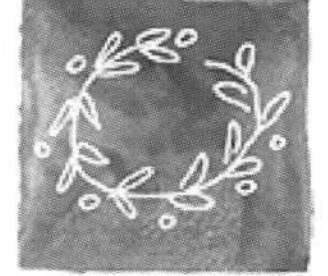

The Olympic games, the ultimate religious and athletic manifestation of the ancient Greeks, were associated with the sacred olive tree, as is shown in ancient sources.

Before the opening of the games, the "spondophoroi" (the libation holders) went from town to town transporting the panhellenic message for truce and peace.Before and after the games, every act of violence, fight, even death penalties were postponed.

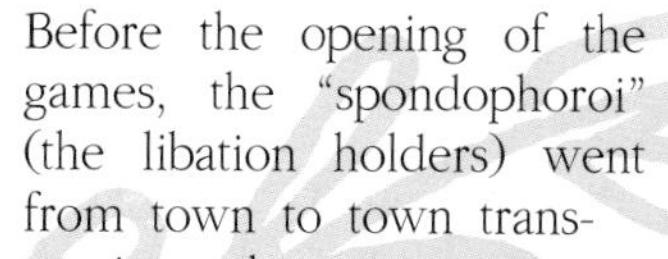

The games lasted for five days. On the final day, all winners stood in front of Zeus' temple and were crowned with garlands made with branches from the sacred olive tree that was next to the temple. That wreath was the greatest reward an athlete could obtain in ancient Greece! Its profound significance is manifested in a dialogue between certain Persian officers who had invaded Greece and had been defeated at Thermopyles. The following dialogue is reported to us by Herodotus, one of the most ancient historians:

The Persians wanted to know what the prize was in the Olympic games and they were told that the winners were crowned with an olive branch wreath! Then one of them exclaimed:

"Alas, against what sort of people have we come to fight! They are people who do not fight for money, only for virtue"!

It was exactly that virtue that was represented by the humble, yet precious, branch from Zeus' wild olive tree at Olympia!

Olympia, the birthplace of the Olympic Games!

OLIVES AS A FOOD

Even in prehistoric times, the olive was well known as a food. In the beginning there was not the knowledge regarding the processing or the soaking of olives. It was natural in early societies for the olive to be seen as a seasonal type of food. In other words, olives were only consumed during the period when they ripened and became edible. So it follows the first olives to be eaten were the ones that ripened on the trees naturally. With the passing of time, the inhabitants of the Mediterranean areas, who looked upon the olive as an essential part of their diet, developed various methods of keeping olives for a long period of time after the point of harvesting. Several forms of soaking and preservation were developed. For many centuries, a basic ingredient used in the preservation of olives was salt and as additional ingredients they used honey, olive oil, vinegar and vine juice (which could easily be made into wine and wine in turn could be made into vinegar). Aromatic plants were used as preservers but also as a way of improving the flavour of the oil.

Ancient techniques of soaking the bitterness out of the olives survived for many centuries. Some of these methods are still used today! The farming population has hardly modernized the production of edible olives.

For many years, the olive remained a foodstuff of the farming communities, nomads, travellers and the army. Apart from being food of the farming classes, olives were one of the most important appetizers in the ancient world. For this reason, olives were also used on patients as a form of therapy, especially in cases which showed symptoms of lack of appetite. Olives were the favourite starter of the Romans. They were served as a starter at the beginning of a meal at a rich symposium. But as they were loved so much and the greed at Roman symposiums knew no limit, olives were also served for dessert! Lunch or dinner started and ended with olives!

OLIVES IN THE FASTING OF THE ORTHODOX CHURCH

The Orthodox Church requires bodily cleansing prior to big holidays, such as Christmas, Easter and 15th August. Such demands are also made whereby fasting is required on other days in monasteries, on Wednesdays and Fridays. On these days, animal based products are forbidden. Big feasts even disallow the consumption of olive oil but not the olives themselves.

The use of the olive as an allowed food product during times of fasting has proved to be invaluable for long periods of the year. For this reason, monasteries have developed production techniques and consider the olives, like wine and wheat (bread), to be the items which should never be missing from the cellars of a monastery. Pierre Bellon who travelled through Greece in 16th century noted that the basic food of the monks on Mount Athos was salted olives, broad beans and greens. The great Cretan writer Nikos

Kazantzakis described the lives of the hermits who lived in the caves:

"A basket is hung near the sea and when a boat passes by, a little bread and some olives are thrown in ... ... so as not to leave the hermits to die of hunger..."

TRADITIONAL GREEK VARIETIES

In Greece, there is a long tradition in the production of the ripe black olive, of which there are many varieties, in comparison to other olive cultivating countries, such as Spain, where they concentrate on the green olive. The easiest and most natural olive to be consumed by man was the ***throumba*** or ***stafidolia***, in other words, a ripe olive which loses its bitterness on its own with natural processes on the tree. But there are other types of olives such as the *charaktes* (slit) ones and those in vinegar or oil or brine which are still favourites of Greeks. In many Greek areas, soaking techniques for green olives have been known for a long time.

Types of olives depend on their final usage. There are some olives which are only for eating whereas others are for oil making. Many regions in Greece cultivate olives which can be used for both. As some large olives do not provide a good quality of oil, Greek farmers separate their crops in order to produce good quality harvests.

GREEK TABLE OLIVES

Konservolia

This is the most famous Greek variety of table olives. It makes up about 80% of table olive production in Greece. This variety is grown in Central Greece and is known by the name of the area producing it, that is, olives of Amfissa, Agrinion, Volos, Atalanti, Aghios Konstantinos, Stylida etc. The fruits are of medium to large size (weighing between 5 and 8 or even 12 grams). They are round to oval, preserved in brine and have many different brand names.

Nychati of Kalamata

This is one of the most important Greek table olive varieties. It is produced in the south and south-western region of the Peloponnese and particularly in Messinia and Laconia as well as in Central Greece. The fruit is of medium size (3-6 grams). They are black olives and their oil content is 25%. They are used for the preparation of slit olives preserved in brine and vinegar.

Olives of Chalkidiki

In the last few years, it has become known as a very important variety of table olives. It comes from the peninsula of Chalkidiki, close to Mount Athos. Its fruit is very large and for this reason the variety is known as "gaidourolia" (donkey olive).

Megaritiki

This is a dual-purpose variety, used for both oil production and eating. It is cultivated in the region of Attica. Its fruit is small and used mainly for the preparation of black dry-salted olives or of green cracked (tsakistes) olives.

Kothreiki

This is also a dual-purpose variety, produced in the Greek Mainland. Its fruit is similar in colour and shape to the fruit of the konservolia variety.

Karydolia

It is considered to be a clone of the konservolia variety and is grown in the region of Euboea.

Olives of Egumenitsa

This, too, is considered to be a clone of the konservolia variety producing a fruit of smaller size and grown in the area of Egumenitsa (Epirus).

Throumba, throumbolia

The fruit of this variety is of small to medium size and loses its bitterness and becomes sweet on the tree during ripening. The tree thrives on Crete, the Aegean islands or the region of Attica. The loss of bitterness is due to the activity of a fungus growing on the skin of the olive fruit. This variety is used for the production of throumba black olives (see below).

Stafidolies (throumba olives). An excellent produce!

The stafidolies (wrinkled olives) or throumba olives are very special and important edible olives, very close to the present dietary requirements, as they are edible without the addition of much salt. The fruit is a natural product needing no processing to lose its bitterness. The olives mature on the tree and it is from there they are picked manually. Lately the harvesting method has become simpler. Wide nets are spread out under the trees, the olives are knocked down onto them and are collected from there more easily. Then they are washed thoroughly, spread outdoors to dry and finally they are packed under a vacuum with the addition of a small quantity of solid salt to improve their taste. They can alternatively be packed into containers filled with good quality olive oil, without salt. These days they are preserved for months in the freezer without any salt. They should be taken out of the freezer a few minutes before they are consumed. These olives are wrinkled and probably for this reason many people do not like them. Nevertheless, the conscious consumers do not take this "disadvantage" into consideration, as their advantages from the nutritional point of view are so many.

Modern views for less salt in the diet can be a serious reason for the propagation of this absolutely natural and healthy product.

Other Greek table olive varieties

There are some more Greek varieties of table olives which are not available on the market today.

You can discover olives of excellent quality throughout Greece (such as the cracked olives known from even antiquity, or the ***kolymbathes***, which have a long history themselves).

You can try the small Cretan olives prepared from the "tsounati" variety, olives flavoured with herbs, bitter orange, orange etc., olives preserved in olive oil and many others. Unfortunately, they are not all available on the market.

PROCESSING OF TABLE OLIVES

The methods of curing edible olives at home vary, but they are all based on the techniques known from ancient times. For the varieties which do not mature on the tree, the traditional processing requires soaking in water with salt or ashes.

Slitting the olive lengthwise with a sharp knife as well as cracking the flesh open, usually with a wooden object, being careful not to touch the pit, are methods used even today in many Greek areas.

This procedure varies depending on the type of olives and how ripe they are.

The traditional methods of curing edible olives have been modernized and give excellent natural products.

HOW TO MAKE YOUR OWN TABLE OLIVES!

Kalamata slit olives in olive oil

If you can find black olives of the Kalamata variety, try this traditional recipe. These olive fruits are large and are gathered when they are deep black but before they are wrinkled. Select firm and unbruised olives. Incise the olives

lengthwise in two places with a sharp knife without touching the stone. Place them into a large clay or plastic vase with enough water to cover them for about 12 days changing the water daily until they are no longer bitter. Prepare brine with 1 litre water and 100 grams salt for every kilo of olives, put the sweetened olives in the brine and leave them for two days. Then drain them and soak in vinegar where you have added a little water (4 parts of vinegar to 1 part of water) for another two days. Finally drain them again and store in glass or clay jars covered with olive oil. Season with bay leaves or oregano, if desired.

According to another method, after drawing out the bitterness, store them in brine acidified with vinegar, 3 parts of brine to 1 part of vinegar. (To prepare the brine, dissolve 100 grams of salt in a litre of water). Cover with a layer of olive oil, 1 cm thick, and seal the jars.

How to make cracked (tsakistes) olives

These olives are harvested as early as October, while they are still green, unripe.
Crack each olive open carefully with a wooden object (usually a hammer) trying not to crack the stone, only the flesh. Soak them in water for 10 days changing the water daily until they lose their bitterness.
When they become sweet, store them in brine prepared with 1 litre of lukewarm water and 100 grams of salt for every kilo of olives. Add 3/4 cup of lemon juice and various herbs, such as oregano, coriander, fennel, slices of lemon, hot pepper etc., according to taste. Cover with a layer of olive oil, 1 cm thick.
Cracked olives should be consumed within a short period of time because they may bleach or get mouldy with the passing of time.
Serve sprinkled with coriander, chopped garlic, slices of lemon and olive oil mixed with lemon juice.

❖ ATTENTION:

The jars in which the olives are stored should be put in a cool, dark place so that they can be kept for up to a year. They can also be kept in the fridge.
Before using them, it is best to re-wash them in water and then drain them. They can be eaten on their own as a starter with bread or cheese, in salads, in various dishes, in bread or even as a paste.

Scented olives

Whether your own or bought, olives can be scented, depending on your preferences with fennel, coriander, oregano, thyme, rosemary, bay leaves, hot peppers, garlic, lemon, orange rind or other herbs.

2 cups olives
1 clove garlic
2 hot peppers
1 quartered lemon
1 tbsp rosemary (or any other herb)
2 tbsp vinegar
1 cup olive oil

Mix olives with garlic, hot peppers, lemon and rosemary in a bowl. Beat olive oil with vinegar. Pour over the olives and make sure they are covered. These can be kept in a jar or the fridge for quite a while.

OLIVE PASTE

It was quite usual in ancient times to consume olive paste, either made from whole olives or from what was left of the olives after pressing. So the idea that olive paste is something new is quite unjustified, as it was common place in classic times and also could have quite possibly gone on, long before then. Calimachus the Cyrenaeus, who wrote in the first decades of 3rd century B.C., states clearly that olives can produce a ground mash.

Olive paste can be used in place of butter in breakfast (to spread on bread) or as an appetizer before a meal.
To make olive paste, mash the olives and scent them again, depending on your preferences, whether coriander, cumin, oregano, mint, fennel, thyme, garlic, onion, hot pepper, lemon or other herbs.

Olive paste with fennel and mint

1 cup pitted black olives
2 tbsp finely chopped fennel or 1 tbsp fennel seeds, roasted and ground
1 clove garlic
2 tbsp fresh or dried mint
1 hot pepper
1 tbsp lemon or fresh orange juice
1 tbsp good quality vinegar
4 tbsp olive oil

Put the ingredients in a blender to make a paste. Keep it in the fridge but let it stand for 2-3 hours before using it. It can be stored for a few days.

Olive paste with oregano

As above.

WHAT IS OLIVE OIL?

Olives are the fruits of the olive tree, which is indigenous to the Mediterranean countries but also cultivated nowadays in other areas, even in America and Australia. There are many different kinds of olives. Some are used only for making oil, while others are for eating and these are usually large in size. There are also some varieties which are used for both oil and consumption.

The tree blossoms in Spring (April - May) and shortly afterwards, the olives start to grow. They are a bright green colour to begin with and this lasts until the point when they ripen. This point varies amongst the different types of olives but usually it is around the end of autumn.

The olive is a drupe, in other words, a fruit with a fleshy skin enclosing a stone and either circular or oval in shape.

Olive oil is the natural juice of the olive, a pure product which is obtained with machinery, by natural means.

The oil of the olive is found in the pericarp, the fleshy part of the fruit.

❖ **ATTENTION:**

There is a great difference between olive oil and seed oil when looking at its make-up and how it is obtained. Seed oil is produced from various seeds put through chemical procedures. Olive oil is only from the olive and is made in a totally natural way.

THE OLIVE HARVEST AND OLIVE OIL PRODUCTION

Olive cultivation is, relatively speaking, easy. It requires no specific farming care and the most difficult thing is collecting the fruit. It has been calculated that the gathering of olives takes 60% of the total cultivation costs of olives! It is a tough tree which thrives easily.

Olive harvesting in older times on the island of Lesbos. Painting by Stratis Axiotis (from Th. Paraskevajidis' book, "The olive trees and the farmers on Lesbos").

The harvesting of olives used to be done by hand in the old days when production was not so great. The olives were allowed to drop and then they were collected. For those olives which didn't fall, the tree was shaken or hit with a stick until they did and then the women, who usually had this tiring job, collected them and put the fruit in baskets or panniers as can be seen in ancient Greek and Byzantine pictures. This method does not produce a good quality of oil. The traditional way of harvesting olives in areas of large production was the one using the stick. Special sticks were used to beat the trees so that the olives fell into special tarpaulins or nets that had been placed under the tree. In some areas with relatively small levels of production, it was customary to "pluck" the branches, in other words, to pull the olives off by hand and place the fruit in big baskets. This is probably the best method as you then do not bruise the olive, but this way would be impossible for large-scale harvesting. Recent years have seen the appearance of some machines for harvesting purposes. These use the idea of a mechanised stick beating the tree, thus helping production to increase. There are small, plastic sticks which rotate on the machinery. They release the olives from the branches and the fruit fall down onto the prepared nets. Olives were taken to the oil press in large sacks in the old days. However, they lose their value if kept in these sacks for many days. It has therefore been established that olives need to be pressed one or two days after having been harvested. Nowadays, olives are transferred in plastic boxes, which do not bruise or press the fruit and are taken to the press on the same day they are collected.

Ancient olive press installations from the Minoan palace of Phaestos.

OLIVE PRESSING

History

Stone base of an old oil mill from John Papadakis' private collection, Axos, Mylopotamos, Crete.

Information about olive oil pressing in prehistoric times is not clear. The olive oil that was needed by each family seems to have been produced in small home environment. Olives were squashed in stone vessels and, by adding water, the oil could be removed, as it floated on the surface of the water.

At a later stage, people crushed olives im-between large circular stones which rotated so that pulped olives produced oil along with the other natural juices of the fruit. Being lighter, oil floated and was easily collected. Slowly but surely, the pressure which had been carried out by stone was replaced with

Engraving of the year 1793, when horses were used for the rotation of the pressing stones.

machinery which had a lever. Pressing the olive pulp caused the oil to yield, along with the other juices. A picture from an oil press dating back to 6th century B.C. which worked using levers, was found on Santorini. The lever was

An olive press rotated by horses and an Italian olive press of the 18th century. (Source: Museo dell' Olivo, Imperia).

set in a sturdy place, such as a wall, so that on pressing it, the olive pulp was crushed, so producing the oil. As years went by, new types of presses were created which were able to crush evenly.

Until the first decades of the 20th century, the extraction of olive oil from the fruit was a difficult procedure. Olives were pressed on threshing floors where two large mill-stones were rotated.

These were pulled by animals which trod around the stones. The pulp was then taken, a mixture of juices, oil and the pit, to be placed in cloth sacks. These sacks were piled up on top of each other and placed in the press. The pressure forced out the liquids (oil and water).

At certain villages in Cyprus, when the production was poor, olives were pressed in old open-air olive factories where the stone was rotated by hand! There were also open-air olive presses for crashing the olives and selecting the olive oil. (Source: Xen. Lazarou, Antilaloi Kypriakis Ypaithrou).

The oil, being lighter, floated on the water and was easy to collect. The use of electricity put an end to the labour of the animals and the use of centrifugal power made the business of olive pressing much easier.

Left: An olive press of 19th century. (Monastery of Hodeghitria, Messara, Crete).

Modern methods. The "synolea" method

Today, technology has created the best conditions for olive pressing and extraction of olive oil. The crushing is done by machinery. Special metal hammers mush the olives and there then follow various ways of oil extraction. Centrifugal power is one of those methods. The most recent way is the "synolea" method. First the olives are crushed and then special blades plunge quickly and steadily into the olive pulp. Olive oil drops rest on them, due to adherence, and these are collected. This technique produces an excellent product which retains its natural character. In general, this type of olive oil keeps its scent intact and is much tastier.

From the olive tree to the olive oil; drawing of the International Olive oil Council. Above: Olive harvesting.

Below: Crashing of the olives with rotating stones and production of olive oil by pressing the olive pulp.

STORAGE OF OLIVE OIL

Above: Storage of olive oil inside stainless containers at the Monastery of Toplou, Siteia, Crete.

The storage of olive oil in glass bottles is an ideal solution in order to retain its natural character for several months, especially if the bottle is dark in colour. Olive oil is sensitive to light oxidation, which speeds up when its colouring substances come in contact with sunlight, room light, even light from fluorescent lamps. For this reason, if the bottle is transparent, it

Right: Selling olive oil; representation on a vessel of 5th century B.C.

An olive oil merchant on a gravure of 12th century.

should be kept in a dark place. Ideal storage temperature is believed to be 10-15° Celsius.

❖ ATTENTION:

Olive oil should not come into contact with metal, especially copper and iron. These metals speed up the process of acidic deterioration of the product. Storage is allowed only in non-oxidising metal containers.

Old jars for the storage of olive oil (19th-20th century).

OLIVE OIL QUALITIES
Practical advice

Olive oil grading follows international quality standards according to the method of production, the level of acidity and basic organic characteristics. Special testers check the taste and smell of an oil. These characteristics in connection with colour, are the three areas checked by international testers in assessing the quality level of a product. Fluidity and a harmonious - balanced relationship between the characteristics of the oil, are used to form a final evaluation.

❖ Colour

Colour does not always prove the quality of an oil. A good oil can be from green to golden yellow. It can even seem cloudy if it has not settled yet. As colour is not a sure sign of quality, experts test olive oil in dark blue and not transparent glasses.

The colour of the product depends on the main substances of the olive fruit that the oil has been made from. If chlorophyll is the main factor, then the oil will lean more towards the colour green. If carotene is the main substance, then the oil will be more golden yellow.

Olives which are gathered at the beginning of the harvesting period, usually produce oil of a greener colour, due to the chlorophyll they contain.

❖ Taste and smell

Olive oil reminiscent of the scent either of fruit or of oil fresh from pressing is believed to be excellent. This is the same with wine, as testers try to pinpoint pleasant smells which remind them of other products, such as fruit, like apples or nuts, etc. The smell and taste are due to a large amount of scenting agents which give the consumer the idea of fresh fruit.

A bitter or slightly bitter taste shows that the olives used were not ripe when picked. A pleasant smell and taste can also be put down to the area in which the olives grew and the way they were cultivated.

A fruit taste comes from ripe olives which have balanced characteristics. Olive oil with an unpleasant smell and taste is better avoided. Smelling soil or mould down-grade a product. It can be seen then that experience is needed for someone to safely assess an oil.

❖ Acidity

The degree of acidity in olive oil indicates the oleic acid content. It is believed to be edible, according to the International Olive Oil Council, when the acidity does not exceed 3.3 degrees (content of oleic acid 3.3%).

In reality, olive oil which has an acidity level of no more than one is much better.

You should always read the label on an olive oil bottle to see the degree of the acidity. In Greece, there is excellent olive oil with acidity less than 0.5 degrees! The degree of acidity greatly affects the taste.

Olive oil with a higher lever of acidity makes its presence known on first tasting it as it has a pungent spicy unpleasant taste. Methods of harvesting, storage and pressing can affect the level of acidity.

Organic olive oil producers transfer olives to the press, not in sacks but in boxes, which do not press or bruise the fruit. Also, producers take care to not store them more than one or two days so that the fruit is not spoilt.

❖ Oxidization

Oxidization (rancidity) is one of the most important causes of spoiling olive oil. Conditions of storage (light, oxygen etc) help oxidization. This is easily spotted by a tester without scientific tests, as the taste is badly affected by oxidization. Olive oil producers can distinguish good quality from rancid olive oil, after years of experience. As they say, "the oil got rancid and smells like soil". On Crete, they identify the smell of rancid olive oil with the smell of soil. Similarly, at Kalavryta of the Peloponnese they say "the oil is not good because it nips the tongue".

Oxidization reduces or destroys the basic components in olive oil, especially those which are unique to this produce, in contrast to all the other fat substances. It can destroy the fat-soluble vitamins or the fatty acids such as linoleic and linolenic but it can also produce substances which are dangerous for the human body.

OLIVE OIL CHARACTERISTICS

These are pinpointed by testers. Try a few different kinds of olive oil. Experience will help you to choose the oil you prefer.

❖ Organic olive oil

Greek olive oil is in general, of good quality. Cultivation methods do not use a lot of fertilizers. The main chemical treatment which is carried out is spraying olive trees at random, in an attempt to combat the olive tree's worst enemy, dacus oleae. It is an olive fruit fly which destroys olive production.

Farmers use chemicals which act as bait, attract the insects and eventually kill them.

Natural cultivation is taken even further when you consider that without these chemicals (fertilizers, pesticides, insecticides), the farmer has to encounter a range of olive tree related diseases. In the last few years, many naturally cultivating olive producers have appeared in Greece. These farmers have made progress and have been internationally recognized.

These olive oil producers provide an oil which is rich in organic characteristics. Olive oil extraction is done under strict conditions of processing, where only mechanical pressing is permitted nor heat in the press and no other techniques are used which might affect its characteristics.

In countries of the European Union (including Greece, of

course), organic products are strongly protected by law and are carefully checked by quality control organizations. Organic oil is usually extra virgin olive oil or just virgin.

❖ **ATTENTION:**
Organic olive oil bought should state on the label, the title BIO.

PRACTICAL ADVICE

Good olive oil has a pleasant taste and smell. In general, virgin olive oil extra should always be chosen. If the level of acidity is mentioned, make sure it is low. International agreement states that virgin olive oil extra should have an acidity level between 0.1 and 1. Recently, some bottles have included exact information regarding this matter (i.e. 0.4 or 0.5). This is a good sign which gives the consumer the choice of a high quality oil or a poor, blended olive oil.

❖ BLENDING

In general, olive oil is technically quite easy to mix with seed oil. This might be done by disreputable traders who sell unbottled olive oil but it is impossible for established oil producers to do something like this when they have their name on the product. It is difficult for a consumer to realize unless he has a great experience in tasting olive oil. Technology now can detect the slightest forgery. So no reputable oil producer would ever endanger his reputation...

❖ **ADVICE:**
Olive oil resembles set fat when below zero degrees Celsius. Seed oils remain liquid at these temperatures. If unsure about the quality of your oil, do your own experiment to see if it is a forgery.

A. VIRGIN OLIVE OIL

In general, virgin olive oil is, regardless of its quality level, a natural product, which has not had its characteristics altered, has been extracted naturally, without chemicals or other processing and the heat during pressing, which does not exceed 33° Celsius, cannot affect its quality.

It is the oil used in most olive oil producing areas in Greece and the same referred to by medical studies, which proved that the Cretan diet is the healthiest in the Mediterranean.

This oil retains all its natural characteristics which have been pressed out of the olive fruit, including various trace elements and vitamins.

❖ 1. Virgin olive oil extra

Exceptional quality olive oil. Particular natural flavour and taste.
Acidity ranges between 0.1-1 (0.1–1 grams oleic acid per 100 grams olive oil).

❖ 2. Virgin olive oil - fine

Olive oil with excellent smell and taste.
Acidity can reach 1.5 grams oleic acid per 100 grams olive oil.

❖ 3. Virgin olive oil semi-fine

A virgin olive oil with a good taste and smell.
Acidity can reach 3.3 grams oleic acid per 100 grams olive oil.

❖ 4. Virgin olive oil lampante

Taste and smell are not good. It cannot be consumed without being refined. Acidity can reach 3.3%.

B. REFINED OLIVE OIL

This comes from the industrial type of oil "lampante". It has a bad smell and taste so it needs to be processed in order to be made edible. The refining eliminates the bad smell and taste so that the oil attains neutral characteristics. The main problem with refined oil is the down-grade of its characteristics and a decrease in its vitamin value as well as other important agents it contains, such as tocopherols and sterols. Refined oil does not have the same bright colour which extra virgin olive oil has. It is light yellow colour without smell or taste which would attract interest, in other words, neutral. The production of refined oil is limited in Greece in comparison with other oil producing countries which use this method on the larger part of their production. Greek olive oil is a high quality product and does not need to be processed in order to be consumed. That is why the inhabitants of areas where high quality olive oil is consumed, find it difficult to accept anything less.

C. PURE OLIVE OIL

It is a product appearing on the market more and more often. It is basically a refined olive oil, to which virgin oil is added to improve its character. Unfortunately there are no set levels of blending refined olive oil with virgin olive oil. Thus, there could be 50% virgin oil in a mixture or just 10%! The neutral refined oil can easily attain an improved colour, taste and smell. Industries that deal with its promotion have come up with their own levels in a mixture so as to improve the quality but at the same time, keep the price down. The Greek consumer who is used to the taste of good virgin olive oil has difficulty in using it... Acidity level may reach 1.5%.

D. OLIVE RESIDUE OIL

Chemical methods (solvents) are used to dissolve oil from the residue. Olive stones are woody and the oil which remains cannot be removed naturally, so it is removed with the use of solvents. Acidity does not exceed 1.5%.

❖ ADVICE:

Extra virgin olive oil may be a little more expensive but the quality is much better. It is a totally natural product which should be used instead of butter in cooking and on salads. It really is a matter of health!

EXTRA VIRGIN OLIVE OIL UP TO 90%!

Greek olive oil producers offer extra virgin olive oil at a percentage of 80-85%. In some areas, such as Crete, this figure is greater, as much as 85-90% and tends to increase!

CHEMICAL COMPOSITION OF OLIVE OIL

Olive oil is a fluid fatty product containing important constituents which give it unique characteristics. Among these are:

- *Organic acids*
- *Vitamins*
- *Colouring substances*
- *Hydrocarbons*
- *Minerals (micronutrients etc.)*

The fatty acids of olive oil are classified into saturated acids (palmitic, stearic etc) and unsaturated acids (oleic, linoleic, linolenic). The unsaturated acids are again classified into mono-nounsaturated and polyunsaturated acids. In general, the unsaturated acids are liquid whereas the saturated are solid. At normal temperatures, olive oil remains liquid and this is due to its large amount of unsaturated compounds.

❖ **The fatty acids contained in olive oil are:**

- *Omega 9 oleic 63-83%*
- *Palmitic 7.0-17%*
- *Palmitoleic 0.3-3.0%*
- *Omega 6 Linoleic 3.5-14%*
- *Stearic 0.5-5.0%*
- *Omega 3 Linolenic 0.01-1.5%*
- *Myristic 0.0-0.1%*
- *Arachidic 0.0-0.8%*

Olive oils from the more southerly regions of the Mediterranean tend to be higher in linoleic acid than in the northerly regions.

❖ OTHER SUBSTANCES

- ***Tocopherols*** *150-170 mg/kg*

An excellent source of vitamin E. They protect against LDL oxidation (peroxidation, a dominant risk factor for the development of atheromatosis).

- ***Phenols, polyphenols, phenolic acids***

They have an important antioxidative effect and protect olive oil from high temperatures.

- ***Sterols** and especially **ß sitosterol***

This can only be found in olive oil. Its effect is extremely important as it counters intestinal absorption of dietary cholesterol.

- ***Hydrocarbons (squalene, ß-carotene etc.)***

These also have an antioxidative effect. Recent studies have shown that substances like squalene can even lessen the rate of growth of breast cancer and may be other cancers.

- ***Alcohols (terpenic alcohols)***

It is believed to help the distancing of cholesterol through the increase of bile production.

❖ The **colouring substances** in olive oil are:

- **ß-carotene**
- **a-chlorophyll**
- **ß-chlorophyll**

These substances are extremely useful in metabolism, cell renewal and wound healing.

❖ CALORIC VALUE

1 grammar olive oil gives 9.3 calories.
1 tbsp olive oil contains 14 grams fat and gives 120 calories.
Olive oil should take the place of other oils and fats in cooking. It should be used instead of butter and it is the only oil that can be used in frying (it is resistant to heating a lot more than the other oils). However, it should not be taken in addition to the consumption of other fats, because there is the possibility of gaining weight.

❖ ABSORPTION OF OLIVE OIL

Olive oil is easily digested. The human body absorbs the vitamins contained in this natural olive juice. Research has proved that only breast milk can be absorbed more easily by the human body! The make up of fat in breast milk is similar to that in olive oil.

WHY OLIVE OIL ONLY?

Olive oil should be used instead of any other fat on the market. It is the only one produced in a natural way and it keeps its characteristics intact. Seed oil is the result of chemical processes! In other words, there is no room for comparison.
Various myths have been circulated that seed oil is lighter or better than olive oil but this has proved completely false in scientific research.

❖ Olive oil is not heavier than any other oil, as all the fat agents have nearly all the same calories! In addition, olive oil is rich in antioxidative agents (those which have an anti-cancer effect) while medical studies point out the health value to people.

WHICH OLIVE OIL?

Without doubt, the best olive oil is the extra virgin one. It is actually olive juice. It can be used for cooking, in place of animal fats and other fatty substances. It can be used on bread, in place of butter or on salads. A little bread (usually a dried rusk) soaked with olive oil has always been a good solution for a Greek's breakfast or a snack. On Crete, the island where the inhabitants, according to the World Health Organization and other medical studies in the last forty years, have the best health, dipping bread in olive oil is common practice. Villagers can be seen to eat salads with fresh vegetables "swimming" in olive oil and at the end, bread is used to wipe up the last of the olive oil! Extra virgin olive oil is a little more expensive than virgin oil, more expensive than "pure olive oil" (a blend of virgin and refined olive oil) and definitely more expensive than refined oil. But the difference in the price is not so great to be unaffordable.

❖ **GENERALLY:** *Extra virgin olive oil is not expensive. As a valuable ally in health, it is worth much more than the price paid.*

GREEN COLOURED OLIVE OIL

This will probably have been made from green olives which have been collected before having ripened and sometimes, as has already been mentioned, the colour is a result of other factors, too. Usually, green-coloured olive oil is more pepper-like in taste. It can be used for cooking pulses and vegetables, game or meat, although it is a matter of personal choice.

GOLDEN-YELLOW OLIVE OIL

This probably comes from olives that had started to turn reddish or black. It generally has a milder taste, more fruity and gives off a variety of aromas. The smell may be reminiscent of fruit or vanilla. This is the oil usually chosen by chefs especially when cooking fish. But all these points are matters of personal choice. Good extra virgin olive oil can be used for many purposes, even for sweets or cakes. In traditional Greek cooking, only olive oil is used for this baking and the oil is generally of a very high standard.

HOW TO JUDGE EXTRA VIRGIN OLIVE OIL?

A wise consumer should read the label on olive oil containers. These give details that will help to make the right choice. The colour may range from green to golden-yellow but this is never a sure sign of quality. So, always read the label on the outside, ***EXTRA VIRGIN OLIVE OIL,*** then look at various other points:

1. Date of bottling and expiry date. In other words, the period of time an oil producer can guarantee his product. Olive oil can last for up to a year and a half in a good container, even a little longer.

2. Level of acidity. The degree of acidity is now printed on the outside label. The consumer can then ascertain what he wants to buy. Olive oil with an acidity level less than 5 is considered excellent.

3. Area of production. Region and country of origin. There are many areas known for their good olive oil. Shouldn't we know them?

4. The amount in the container. Work out the price per litre.

5. Especially for organic olive oil, take care that there is the exact indication on the label that has been established for organic products. Look for a guarantee from an organization.

6. The trade name is not enough. Know the name of the oil producer or company. A responsible producer always ensures that there is information about the product so that it reaches you in the best condition.

The extra virgin olive oil has its own distinct smell and taste and so cannot be neutral. Olive oil with no taste and of a light colour is usually a product of refining.

OLIVE OIL, THE SECI

It is known world-wide that olive oil acts as a shield of protection regarding our health, when taking into account cardiovascular diseases, cancer, even diabetes and other diseases. More and more research is being carried out which shows the great value of olive oil as a perfect food for man.

❖ **BAD CHOLESTEROL:**
The consumption of olive oil, instead of other fats or oils, reduces the concentration of LDL cholesterol in the blood without decreasing the levels of HDL, the so-called "bad" and "good" cholesterol respectively!

❖ **TRIGLYCERIDES:**
It has been shown that olive oil reduces the level of triglycerides in the blood.
A collection of bad cholesterol and triglycerides in the blood can block the arteries which transport oxygen to the brain and heart.
In general, olive oil protects against heart diseases.

❖ **HYPERTENSION:**
Olive oil reduces blood pressure, both systolic and diastolic. Therefore it decreases the risk of heart attacks and strokes.

T OF GOOD HEALTH

❖ **CANCER:**

Recent studies have shown that olive oil consumption can slow down breast cancer and other types of cancer. A balanced diet with olive oil and vegetables can reduce the chances of the appearance of cancer by 75%.

❖ **GASTROINTESTINAL SYSTEM:**

Recent research shows that olive oil in conjunction with a healthy diet (vegetables, little meat etc)

- protects against cancer of the stomach
- makes the liver work better
- helps the liver to detoxify poisonous substances

❖ **OSTEOPOROSIS:**

Olive oil assists in the maintenance of bone density and protects against osteoporosis.

❖ **RHEUMATOID ARTHRITIS:**

Olive oil consumption reduces the chances of the appearance of this condition by 75%, especially with a balanced diet and the consumption of more fish.

❖ **DIABETES:**

Olive oil should also be included in the treatment of diabetes.

OLIVE OIL IN COOKING

SCENTED OILS

Scented oils have been prepared in Greece since the Bronze Age (for 4000 years now). They were usually intended for cosmetic purposes, but there is evidence that they were also used in cooking.

Ancient traditions could not be forgotten easily. There is no full picture as to how this practice continued through the centuries or if it was forgotten totally in some areas but it seems to have survived in some areas of Crete...

In the area of Kastelli, Pediada, on Crete, up until the first few decades of the 20th century at least, they used to put a bunch of oregano in the jar with the oil which was to be used for cooking.

HOW TO MAKE SCENTED OLIVE OIL

Scented olive oil can be made using aromatic plants, fresh or dried, spices, garlic, hot pepper, or the peel of citrus fruits. These could be used on their own or in combination with others.

The olive oil to be used has to be of good quality and of low acidity. In order to accept the scents of the herbs or the other ingredients, the oil should not have its own strong smell. Some use refined olive oil or pure olive oil because it is neutral in taste. In this way though, the advantages of extra virgin olive oil are lost. Extra virgin olive oil with a mild taste can therefore be used. The results are wonderful, as a totally natural product is consumed with all its benefits.

Bottles used for storage should be clean and dry. The aromatic plants used should also be clean and dry.

The bottles with olive oil should not be left in the sun but kept in dark, cool places.

Scented oil can serve as a lovely starter when on small dried rusks or bread. It is the best substitute for butter and it has no cholesterol. It can also be added to salads, boiled vegetables, roasted meat or fish, rice, potatoes, pastry and also used as a basic ingredient of sauces.
Slices of bread drizzled with scented olive oil, such as with rosemary, garlic or hot pepper, can be browned in the oven or on the grill.
Naturally, olive oil has an array of smells but, by experimenting with aromatic plants in different combinations, a choice of scent can be made. It is not a bad idea to have a few bottles of scented olive oil to be used for different purposes.

If you want to quickly scent olive oil, heat the aromatic plants in a small amount of olive oil, then filter through a clean cloth and add to the main body of oil.

Olive oil with aromatic plants

Olive oil can be scented with all types of aromatic plants: rosemary, fennel, dill, mint, basil, parsley etc. A bottle of olive oil can be scented with a sprig of each of these plants or two or three together.
If using only one plant, place 2-3 sprigs, washed and dried, in a bottle with 2 cups of olive oil.
Store the bottle in a cool, dark place for about ten days before using it.
The plants can be left in the bottle to add to the scent visually, but not for too long, as they can spoil the oil. Thus it is better to remove the plants once the olive oil is scented.
Olive oil scented with mint, parsley and fennel or dill is very successful.

Olive oil scented with fennel

In a bottle, put 2 cloves of garlic, which is optional, 2-3 cloves and 3-4 sprigs of fennel which has been washed and dried.
Depending on the season, fennel seeds can be used and 1 tablespoon is enough. Add a litre of olive oil and leave for 2 weeks before using.

Olive oil scented with oregano

In a bottle with 2 cups olive oil, place 2-3 sprigs of fresh oregano or 2 tablespoons of dried herb, cap the bottle tightly and store in a dark, cool place.
It can be used after 10 days and can be added to anything, from salads to meat and fish.
The smell of this oil is similar to the one with basil. It can also be complemented with lemon.

Olive oil scented with oregano, thyme, mint and basil

In a large bottle olive oil, about 4 cups, you can place many herbs together such as 2-3 sprigs of oregano, 1 teaspoon thyme, 1 teaspoon dried mint and 1 teaspoon dried basil.
The result, after several days, is a superbly scented oil which can be used for many dishes.
The oil can be filtered through a cloth or coffee filter to remove the herbs.

Olive oil scented with basil

In a bottle, put 3-4 sprigs of basil which has been washed and dried, along with 2 cloves of garlic, which is optional. Add 2 cups of extra virgin olive oil and cap the bottle tightly. The scented oil will be ready in about 10 days.

Olive oil with basil goes perfectly with uncooked vegetables but especially tomatoes. (Imagine slices of tomatoes topped with feta cheese or sour mizithra and drizzled over with basil scented oil). It also goes well in tomato sauces and is superb for dunking pieces of bread.

Olive oil scented with citrus fruits

In a bottle with 2 cups of olive oil, put the peel from half a lemon and half an orange and cap tightly. The oil is ready in 10 days. Remove the peel after 2 months to keep the oil longer. Store in a dark, cool place.

Olive oil scented with citrus fruits is wonderful on salads, boiled greens, fish or meat, or to scent cakes or sweets such as tarts or biscuits.

Citrus fruits can be combined with other aromatic plants.

Oil scented with oregano and lemon peel or thyme and lemon peel is a great success.

Olive oil with garlic

Mash 4 cloves of garlic and mix with 4 tablespoons of olive oil in a blender.
Filter this through a cloth or a coffee filter and transfer to a bottle with 2 more cups of olive oil. It should be kept in a cool, dark place.
Olive oil scented with garlic goes perfectly with grilled slices of bread, spaghetti, soups, sauces, roasted meat and fish, salads and uncooked vegetables.

Olive oil scented with lemons

Clean and dry three small lemons. Place 3 cloves in each lemon.
Put these in a jar and add 1 litre of olive oil.
Keep in a dark, cool place.

Olive oil with garlic and rosemary

In a bottle with 2 cups of olive oil, put 2 cloves of garlic, 1 sprig of fresh rosemary and 5-6 peppercorns.
Cap the bottle tightly and keep in a dark, cool place.
When you start to use the oil, after about 10 days, remove garlic and rosemary.
The scent of rosemary can go with other smells. It is wonderful with roast potatoes, aubergines, lamb or marinated fried fish.

Olive oil with hot peppers

In a bottle with 2 cups of olive oil add 2-3 dry hot peppers or fresh ones to scent the oil which can be used with many dishes. This can be enhanced by adding various spices to produce the oil to your taste.
Use after about 2 weeks and keep in a cool place away from the rays of the sun.

It can be used to accompany greens, meat, especially that which is grilled, as well as omelets and tomato sauces used in pastries, meat and all kinds of pulses.

Olive oil with hot peppers and bay leaves

To the previous oil, 3-4 bay leaves can be added, having been washed and dried first.

Olive oil scented with spices

Two cups of olive oil can be scented with 5-6 peppercorns, 4-5 pimento pods, 1 teaspoon cumin and a stick of cinnamon. This scented oil is suitable for spicy dishes.

Olive oil with cinnamon and clove

In a bottle with 2 cups of oil, put 2-3 sticks of cinnamon and 5-6 cloves. Store the bottle and use the oil after a few days, especially in sweet dishes.

Olive oil and vinegar

This can be made with the same ingredients and combinations used in making scented oil.
The ratio of oil to vinegar depends on personal taste. Normally a ratio of 3:1 is used.

OLIVE OIL IN THE PRESERVATION OF FOOD

Olive oil plays a leading role in the preservation of food, the tasty products which are kept in jars or bottles. Together with vinegar and salt, it has been used to preserve food since ancient times. It is a natural product for preservation as it blocks air from coming into contact with the food. That is why food is placed in oil or it is covered with a thick layer of oil for protection.

Although today we can find all fruits nearly all year round, jars with pickled products in the kitchen are always thought well and offer variety at the table. The season for each fruit or vegetable can be exploited as it is then at its cheapest.

Many kinds of food can be kept in olive oil: meat, fish, vegetables, cheese. Products to be preserved should be completely dry, as water favours the growth of microorganisms.

Also, the jars must be clean and dry. Boil them in water and then leave to dry on a clean towel or in the oven for a while. Fill jars when cool. Close with a lid which has been cleaned as above.

To preserve vegetables, they must be fresh and of good quality. Usually they are boiled for a few minutes in vinegar and then covered in olive oil.

The vinegar should not be of a dark colour in order not to colour the vegetables. Salt should not be left out so that they do not soften.

The jar should not be filled to the

brim but a small space should be left at the top. Don't forget to put a label on the jar with the date of making and contents.
If you keep the jars in the fridge, the oil will thicken but it returns to normal if it is left at room temperature for a while.

Sun-dried tomatoes in olive oil

Choose small, ripe and firm tomatoes, wash and dry them and cut into two. Place them on the grill or on a wooden surface with the cut side up and salt generously.
Leave the tomatoes in the sun for 5-6 days until completely dried. If there is humidity at night, transfer them indoors. (The tomatoes can also be dried in the oven, at low temperature).
Place the dried tomatoes in sterilized airtight jars, cover with olive oil and tap. You can flavour with one tablespoon fennel seeds, basil or oregano.

Pickled bulbs

Bulbs of the plant *Muscari comosum* are indigenous to the Mediterranean countries. They can be found in many European shops but are difficult to get hold of in other countries. Usually a starter but folklore medicine uses them as a diuretic, a tonic and an aphrodisiac.
Bulbs are now cultivated in many Mediterranean countries.

1 kg bulbs
2-3 teaspoons salt
3 cloves garlic in thin slices or 2-3 fresh garlic leaves, roughly cut

½ cup roughly chopped dill
5-6 peppercorns
2,5 cups white vinegar
½ cup olive oil

Clean the bulbs like the onions and wash them. Boil them for half an hour, changing the water 2-3 times. The last time, add salt. Once cooked, remove from heat and dry on kitchen roll.

Simmer vinegar, garlic, peppercorns and dill and leave to cool. Strain the vinegar and pour over the bulbs which have been put in a jar. Pour in the olive oil and keep in the fridge for quite a while.

They can be eaten drizzled with olive oil and garnished with a little finely chopped dill.

Anchovies or sardines in vinegar and olive oil

Clean the fish removing heads and guts. Place in a bowl with salt and vinegar to cover. (If the vinegar is too strong, dilute with a little water). Leave anchovies in vinegar for about 12 hours and sardines for 24 to 30 hours depending upon their size. Test by pulling the tail and if it moves and the insides are rather white than red, then they are ready. The fish can be filleted or left as they are.

Place the fish in a bowl and cover with olive oil. You can garnish with parsley and thin slices of garlic. They can be kept in the fridge for quite a while.

Octopus in olive oil and vinegar

1 kg octopus
2-3 bay leaves
5-6 peppercorns
½ cup vinegar
½ cup olive oil

Wash the octopus or octopuses and place in a pan with the bay leaves and peppercorns. Cook on a low heat in its own juices until tender. If needed, add vinegar.

Once the octopus has cooled, cut into small pieces and place in a jar. Add vinegar and then olive oil to cover.

Oil that has been scented with garlic is preferred. Close the jar and store in a cool place.

Pickled aubergines in olive oil

1 kg long aubergines
2 cups vinegar
3 teaspoons salt
2 mashed hot peppers
or 1 tablespoon peppercorns
1 small bunch roughly cut celery
3-4 cloves finely chopped garlic
2-3 tbsp dried oregano
2-3 cups olive oil

Clean and wash aubergines. Cut into thin slices and boil for five minutes in a pot with 2 cups vinegar, 6 cups water and 3 teaspoons salt. Drain immediately and leave to cool.
In a jar, place a layer of aubergines, scatter on celery, garlic, oregano, pepper, drizzle a little olive oil and continue this procedure until all the ingredients have been used. At the end, pour in the olive oil to totally cover and close the jar or jars, if one is not enough. They keep for 2-3 months in a cool, dry place and can be eaten after 3-4 days.
*Alternatively, whole small aubergines can be used which can be pickled in the same way.

Pickled beetroot in olive oil and vinegar

1 kg beetroot
4-5 cloves garlic
2 cups vinegar
½ cup olive oil
3 teaspoons salt

Wash beetroot well and boil in water with salt until soft. Dry, peel and cut into slices. Put in a jar with chopped garlic imbetween. Pour in the vinegar and cover with olive oil. Keep in a cool place and wait 2-3 days before using.

SAUCES AND DIPS with olive oil

Olive oil is the basic ingredient in sauces, along with lemon juice, vinegar or eggs. This is also true for dips, those sauces which are thick and almost set and are used as appetizers before a meal, with the apperitif.

Dips are usually eaten with small items such as vegetables, but also cheese and even bread or dried rusks to be dipped into the set sauce. They can even accompany main courses. These not only offer interesting varieties of taste but also encourage a healthy style of eating due to the olive oil used. Although they may seem like a recent gastronomic variety, many of these dips are well known and loved all over Greece. Tzatziki, taramosalata, aubergine salad and many others have, for centuries, had a place in Greek cuisine. In this case we must look to see if there is a grain of truth in the housewife's philosophy, the person who was responsible for the diet of the family in the past. The strict fasting in the Greek Orthodox Lent encouraged cooking to reach new heights, as it was forced to use the fruits of the land and the ingenuity of the Greek housewife. A taramosalata, for instance, made a meal during Lent much tastier, more varied and it could be stored for days. The same can be said for tomato sauce. Humus (chickpea purée) has a special taste and can be seen not only in Greek cookery (especially the islands) but also in various Arabic countries.

Meat could be accompanied by tzatziki or tyrokafteri. The mashed pulses were sometimes the main dishes and at others, the starter. As always, the leading ingredient in all these recipes was olive oil! This could transform a traditional dish into something of great demand, especially in the areas where it was abundant and of good quality. Along with the traditional recipes we can now also add others which have been altered from their original form. Set sauces or dips can be used not only at home but also in places where people gather. These have been used to great effect!

Oil and lemon dressing (latholemono)

1 cup olive oil
1/3 cup lemon juice
1 teaspoon salt
pepper, oregano, thyme or parsley (optional)

Mix all the ingredients together in a jar, tap and shake well.
Use the dressing in salads, on greens, on grilled meat or fish etc.

Oil and vinegar dressing (lathoxitho)

Made in exactly the same way and with the same ingredients as the oil and lemon dressing, only replacing the lemon juice with good vinegar made from wine.
It goes well with fried foods, especially fish or meat, some salads and greens.

Egg-lemon sauce (avgolemono)

It gives flavour and thickens soups and sauces in various dishes.

2 eggs, juice of 2 lemons
2 cups liquid from the food for which avgolemono is prepared

Beat first the whites and then the yolks of the eggs, until frothy, 2-3 minutes. Add lemon juice, beating constantly and then a few ladles of the liquid from the food in the pot until the egg and lemon mixture is warm. Remove pot from heat, pour in egg mixture and shake the pot to mix the egg-lemon mixture with the food.

Yoghurt dip with dill

300 grams strained yoghurt
1 tablespoon dill
1 mashed clove garlic
salt, pepper
2 tablespoons olive oil
1 tablespoon lemon juice

In a deep bowl, beat yoghurt with dill, garlic, salt and pepper. Add olive oil and lemon juice. Beat until well mixed. Keep in the fridge.
This goes well with vegetables and green salads.
Instead of dill, you can use parsley, mint or other herbs.

Parsley dip

1 large bunch parsley (only the leaves)
1 slice stale bread (2 cm thick)
1 small onion
2 cloves garlic
juice of 1 lemon
2 tablespoons olive oil
300 grams strained yoghurt
½ teaspoon salt, pepper

Soak the bread in water, strain and place in a blender with parsley, onion, garlic, salt and pepper. Blend the mixture and then add yoghurt, olive oil and lemon juice and mix. Parsley salad is used either as an accompaniment to fresh vegetables, boiled eggs or fish or alone as a salad, garnished with parsley leaves and olives.

Yoghurt dip with spices

In a large bowl put ½ kilo strained yoghurt and different spices (1/4 teaspoon from each spice). You can use cumin, paprika, coriander or ginger. Add a little salt and, whisking constantly, pour in 6 tbsp olive oil and 2 tbsp lemon juice, one at a time.

Avocado dip

2 avocados
½ teaspoon salt
½ teaspoon pepper
1 small grated onion
2 tbsp finely chopped parsley
2 tbsp lemon juice
2 tbsp olive oil

Peel avocado, remove the stone and then mash it in a deep bowl. Add the other ingredients and beat with a whisk

until creamy. Garnish with parsley and keep the dip in the fridge. Use it on its own to dip appetizers and small vegetable pieces or on meat or fish or even on salads.

Garlic, cucumber and yoghurt dip (tzatziki)

½ kg strained yoghurt
2 large cucumbers
3 cloves garlic
½ teaspoon salt
4-5 tbsp olive oil
2 tbsp vinegar
1 tbsp finely chopped mint or dill (optional)

Peel and grate cucumbers. Squeeze as hard as possible to remove water completely. Mash garlic with salt in a mortar.
In a medium-size bowl, mix yoghurt with cucumber and garlic. Slowly add vinegar and olive oil and combine well. Finally add mint or parsley. Refrigerate until ready to use.

Garlic and potato dip with walnuts (skordalia)

1 kg potatoes
6-8 cloves finely chopped garlic
½ teaspoon salt, ½ cup olive oil
4 tbsp lemon juice or vinegar
150 grams roughly ground walnuts or almonds

Boil potatoes and before they go entirely cold, peel and put them in a blender along with garlic, salt, olive oil and lemon juice or vinegar. At the end, add walnuts or almonds until the mixture becomes creamy. If skordalia is too thick, a little stock from the fish that it usually accompanies can be added. This purée also goes well with fried vegetables.

Aubergine dip

½ kg aubergines
2 mashed cloves garlic or 1 grated medium onion
salt, pepper
2 tbsp finely chopped parsley
1 teaspoon dried oregano
3 tbsp lemon juice
1 tbsp vinegar, 4-5 tbsp olive oil
2 tbsp roughly ground almonds

Wash aubergines and cook in their skins either under the grill or on the cooking ring, having been wrapped in aluminum foil, until they soften. Remove from heat, cool slightly and then peel and remove as many seeds as possible. Place aubergines in a deep bowl and combine with remaining ingredients until smooth. Garnish with olives and capers.

Hot pepper and cheese dip (tyrokafteri)

½ kg crumbled feta cheese*
2 hot green peppers
6 tbsp olive oil, juice of 2 lemons
1 tbsp oregano or finely chopped dill (optional)

First cook peppers in a frying pan with 2 tbsp olive oil or in the oven and blend them in the mixer. While running, add feta cheese, oregano or dill, remaining olive oil and lastly lemon juice until tyrokafteri becomes soft and creamy.

Right: Aubergine dip

** The Greek feta cheese is a unique product exclusively made from sheep's or goat's milk. These animals live freely in the Greek mountains. Feta cheese produced outside Greece is made with cow's milk. The cheese is kept in salty water, cut into blocks, fetes in Greek, wherefrom its name comes.*
The fresh milk is heated on low heat and rennin is added (an enzyme taken from the mucous membrane of the stomach of young animals). When the cheese sets, it is put in wooden containers in order to be strained. Then it is cut into blocks (fetes), salted and packed.

Cod Roe Dip (taramosalata)

In the fasting periods of the Orthodox church, which last for long, some particular dishes are usually made, one of which is taramosalata. It is a traditional food on Clean Monday and the first days of the Holy Week before Easter Sunday. Apart from its use as a food for fasting, it is a well-known Greek appetizer. It is made from cod roe. Cod roe is the preserved eggs from various types of fish such as carp, grey mullet etc. It is sold either packed or loose. There are two types, the pink and the light pink, which Greeks describe as white. The light pink is more expensive but is the best because it does not contain colouring agents.

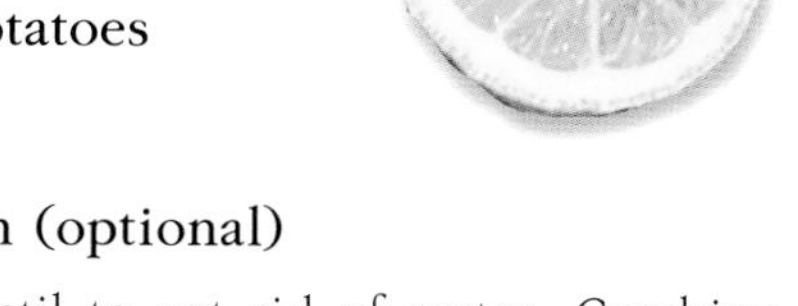

100 grams taramas (cod roe), preferably white
200 grams stale bread
2 medium boiled potatoes
½ cup olive oil
4 tbsp lemon juice
1 small grated onion (optional)

Soak bread and squeeze until to get rid of water. Combine cod roe, potatoes, bread and onion in a mixer. Slowly add olive oil and lemon juice alternatively until taramosalata becomes soft and creamy. Garnish with olives and parsley.

Almond dip with yoghurt

1 kg strained yoghurt
½ teaspoon salt
½ cup finely chopped dill
½ cup whitened, roasted, finely chopped almonds
½ cup olive oil
2 tbsp lemon juice

With a fork or a whisk, beat yoghurt with salt, olive oil and lemon juice. Then add dill and almonds. Combine well.

Chickpea purée - Hummus

A purée of chick peas is well known in many Greek areas as a superb starter. It was even made in ancient Greece and since then, the practice of mashing pulses has become common place in order to make a wide range of main courses and starters.

200 grams chick peas
2 cloves garlic
½ - 1 teaspoon salt

1/3 teaspoon pepper
1/3 teaspoon cumin
3 tbsp olive oil
3 tbsp tahin (ground sesame seeds)
3 tbsp water
4 tbsp lemon juice
1 teaspoon paprika (red pepper)
parsley

Soak chick peas the night before in a large bowl with water. The next day, boil them until soft. Drain and allow to cool. In a bowl, dilute tahin with water. Put chick peas into a mixer

and, grinding constantly, add salt, tahin, garlic, pepper, olive oil and lemon juice until hummus becomes smooth and creamy.
Serve cold, sprinkled with paprika and garnished with finely chopped parsley.

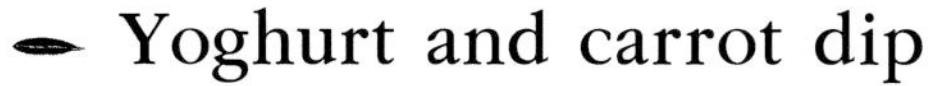

Yoghurt and carrot dip

½ kg carrots
300 grams strained yoghurt
2 cloves mashed garlic
1 teaspoon salt
3-4 tbsp olive oil
1 tbsp lemon juice
½ cup roughly ground walnuts (optional)

Scrape the carrots and grate them (or grind) in the mixer.
Whip yoghurt with remaining ingredients, throw in the carrot and mix well.

OLIVES IN TRADITIONAL COOKING

In Mediterranean cooking, the olive is used to its best in cooking, being the prime ingredient of various delicious starters and renowned for its individual taste. This custom is best seen in the farming communities where it is more readily available. It is mainly consumed in its natural form and can be used to accompany a variety of dishes. Without cooking, the olive is hardly missing from the Greeks' diet. This has made the farming population accustomed to its taste and so they have tried to find different ways of using it in cooking.

Meat stew with olives

1 kg meat (veal, pork, chicken or rabbit)
½ cup olive oil
2 small onions, finely chopped
or 3-4 fresh onions
½ kilo finely chopped tomatoes
½ cup white wine
2 tbsp vinegar
1 cinnamon stick
2 bay leaves
200 grams green olives, cracked or slit
little salt, pepper

Boil the olives for three minutes in water and then get rid of the water. Do the same process again. Then pit the olives.
Wash meat, scone it and brown in a pan with olive oil and onions for 10 minutes. Add wine and vinegar followed by tomatoes, cinnamon, bay leaves and a cup of water. Simmer for about one hour and then add the olives. Continue cooking for another 15 minutes, adding, if needed, a little water.
In the same way, you can cook fish (grouper, cod, sea bream) with olives.

Octopus with olives

1 octopus (1.5 kilos)
½ cup olive oil
1 small onion, finely chopped
½ cup red wine
1 clove finely chopped garlic
1 teaspoon peppercorns
2-3 bay leaves
150 grams green olives

Boil the olives for three minutes in water and pour it out. Do the same process again, then pit the olives.
Wash the octopus and remove eyes, mouth, stomach and ink. Place in a pan and gently cook until all its own juices have evaporated. Then add olive oil and onion until brown. Wine should then be introduced. Add garlic, bay leaves and pepper. Cook for 5-6 minutes and then add olives and a little water. Cook a while longer until it is completely done.

Cuttlefish with olives and spinach

1 kg cuttlefish
1 kg spinach
½ cup olive oil
2 medium-sized dried onions or 5-6 fresh onions
½ cup white wine
1 bunch fennel or dill, finely chopped
½ bunch mint, finely chopped
a little salt, pepper
150 grams olives
1 tbsp flour, juice of 1 lemon

Clean cuttlefish, removing eyes, backbone, stomach and ink. (If desired, keep some of the ink). Re-wash them and cut into pieces. Wash spinach, drain and chop.
Prepare the olives: Boil them in water for about three minutes. Drain them and repeat the process. Then pit the olives.
Brown the onion in olive oil and add dill or fennel, mint and cuttlefish. Cook for 10 minutes and then stir in wine and ink (if desired). Simmer for half an hour and then put in the olives and spinach, very little salt and pepper. Cook for another 10-15 minutes and the dish is ready.

At this point you can thicken the sauce with a diluted solution of one tablespoon of flour with the juice of one lemon. In other words, mix flour with lemon juice, add a little cooking juice from the pan so as to make it dissolve quicker and then put the mixture into the pan. Stir well and cook for five more minutes.

Leeks and celery with olives

½ kg leeks
½ kg celery
½ cup olive oil
1 medium-sized onion, finely chopped
2-3 medium-sized potatoes, cut into quarters
juice of 1 lemon
200 grams pitted olives

Wash leeks and celery and cut into medium-sized pieces. Boil the olives changing the water twice to get rid of the salt. Brown onion in olive oil, add leeks, celery and potatoes along with 1 cup lukewarm water and simmer for about three quarters of an hour. Throw in the olives and cook for 10 more minutes. Add lemon juice and the dish is ready.

Oven Omelet with Spinach and Olives

300 grams spinach, 3 tbsp olive oil
6 eggs, 6 tbsp milk
150 grams grated hard cheese or feta cheese
150 grams pitted olives
100 grams grated toasted bread, salt, pepper

Clean, wash and chop spinach. Then put it in boiling water for 2-3 minutes and drain completely. Heat olive oil in a pan, add spinach and cook for a few minutes until all liquid has evaporated.
Whisk egg yolks with milk and add to the spinach along with cheese, olives, bread crumbs, salt, pepper and the egg whites beaten stiff. Mix carefully and pour the mixture into an oven dish. Bake in medium heat for about 20 minutes or until golden brown.

Tomato sauce with olives

1 medium onion, finely chopped
5-6 tbsp olive oil, 2 cloves finely chopped garlic
½ kg chopped tomatoes
200 grams pitted olives
salt, pepper, oregano, basil
½ cup red wine

Prepare the olives: Boil them in water for about three minutes. Drain them and repeat the process. Finally pit them.
Brown the onion in olive oil in a pan and add garlic, tomatoes, wine, olives, salt, if needed, pepper, oregano and basil. Cook on low heat until the sauce thickens. Use it on spaghetti or on grilled fish.

Cypriot Olive Bread

1 kg flour (preferably wheat flour)
2 packages dry yeast, ½ cup olive oil
1 grated medium-sized onion
1 cup pitted black olives
1 tbsp dried mint, ½ teaspoon salt
lentisk seeds, sesame seeds

Dilute yeast in a large bowl with 1 cup warm water and 1 cup flour to make it have a thick porridge-like appearance. Cover with a towel and leave for about half an hour until it bubbles.

Add salt, onion, olive oil, mint, flour and as much water as is needed (about 2 cups). Knead well and when the dough is soft and seemingly elastic, add the olives. Cover the dough and leave it in a warm place to stand for 2 hours until doubled in bulk. Then form a large loaf of bread or many small ones, round or long, and sprinkle with sesame seeds and lentisk seeds. Place immediately in an oiled baking dish and let stand to rise again. When ready, place in preheated oven and bake for about 45 minutes.

OLIVE OIL IN FRYING

Doctors and dieticians are right with their advice: Fried foods should only be cooked in olive oil! This goes against the myth that animal fats and hydrogenated oils are more resistant to heat in comparison to olive oil. Recent studies have shown that olive oil is the most suitable oil for frying because it remains stable due to its anti-oxidization agents, even at high temperatures.

RESISTANT UNTIL UP TO 250° CELSIUS

Animal fats do not have anti-oxidative agents, so as a result, they are oxidized very quickly, with all the harmful effects to the health of those who consume them. Seed oils contain tocopherols (which are anti-oxidative substances) but the great amount of unsaturated acids they contain makes them to get oxidized quickly when they are heated.

Research which has been conducted in the recent years has shown that seed oils spoil at a temperature of 170-180° Celsius.

On the other hand olive oil can stand temperatures over 200° C. It is even believed that olive oil can stand temperatures of up to 230-250° Celsius! By olive oil, we mean extra virgin olive oil which is more stable due to its anti-oxidative agents, but even refined olive oil has been proved to resist to heat and remain more stable than seed oil!

The chemical substances also which are contained in hydrogenated oils have been shown to increase "bad" cholesterol and to reduce "good" cholesterol levels in blood.

FEWER CALORIES, MORE VITAMINS

Special research studies carried out in the last few years have refuted one more myth. That is the one which states that fried food absorbs too much oil and so it becomes fattening and bad for the health. If someone tries to use a frying pan correctly, then the crispy crust of food seals in the juices and doesn't let the oil into the food. In order to achieve this crispness, the oil should be allowed to heat, almost to "burn" as they say, yet without being over-heated and producing smoke.
Neither should all food be cooked in a frying pan at one time so that the temperature doesn't fall and the frying is done correctly. If the amount of olive oil in the pan diminishes during frying, extra olive oil should be added but only when there is no food in the pan so that the temperature does not drop. It has been proved that foods fried in olive oil absorb less fat in comparison to those fried in seed oils. Therefore, olive oil encourages fewer calories and so it is less fattening! It has also been pointed out that frying doesn't destroy the water-soluble vitamins and the nutritional value of fried food remains almost unaffected.

CAN BE USED MANY TIMES

Olive oil can be used several times for frying, as long as we fry similar things, otherwise the quality of the taste will be affected. But if we fry foods dredged with flour, especially fish, the oil obviously can't be used many times. Yet this oil can be filtered and be used for the frying of similar foods. After 3-5 fries, 30-50% of the vitamins in the olive oil remain unchanged!

Savoury cheese patties

- ***Dough:*** 3 tbsp olive oil
2 eggs
½ teaspoon salt
½ kg all purpose flour
½ cup water
- ***Filling:*** ½ kg grated kefalotyri cheese*
4 eggs

Combine the ingredients for the dough and make a firm mixture. Cover and refrigerate for half an hour. Whisk the eggs and mix in the cheese.

Roll out the dough and cut circles the size of a saucer. Put 1-2 teaspoons of filling on each circle. Fold in two to make a semi-circle and press down the edges so that they stick. This can be done with a fork's prongs. Fry the patties in very hot olive oil and serve sprinkled with grated cheese.

*Kefalotyri: *A hard yellow cheese which is used either as table cheese or grated on various dishes.*

Pancakes

1 cup water, ½ teaspoon salt
1 tbsp lemon juice
1 cup flour
½ cup grape juice syrup or honey or sugar
ground cinnamon, chopped walnuts or sesame seeds

Mix water with salt, lemon juice and flour to achieve a thick batter. Heat olive oil in a frying pan. Drop spoon-size amounts of the batter into the pan. Fry both sides and then place on kitchen roll in order to drain.

Transfer on a plate and pour grape juice syrup or honey over them. Sprinkle with walnuts or sesame seeds and cinnamon. They can even be sprinkled with sugar. You can also add ½ cup of sour mizithra cheese or crumbled feta cheese to the flour mixture.

Small pies with greens

❖ ***Dough:*** 1 cup water
½ teaspoon salt
3 tbsp olive oil
1 tbsp lemon juice
½ kg flour
❖ ***Filling:*** 1 kg greens (spinach, fennel, mint, parsley, leeks, spring onions)
½ cup olive oil, salt, pepper

Prepare the filling: Wash and finely chop the greens. Put olive oil in a pan, heat it and sauté the greens for 10 minutes, adding a little water if needed. Season with salt and pepper and leave in a colander to strain. (They may need quite a few hours, therefore you'd better prepare them the day before and keep refrigerated).

Prepare the dough: Use the above ingredients and knead until you obtain hard dough. Cover and refrigerate for an hour.

Roll out the dough to 2mm thickness, cut out circles the size of a small saucer and fill each one with a teaspoon of the filling. Fold each circle in two and press down the edges with the prongs of a fork. Fry in very hot olive oil.

Courgette balls

1 kg courgettes
2 grated medium-size onions
2 eggs
1 cup finely chopped parsley
½ cup grated cheese
½ cup ground toasted bread
salt and pepper
flour and olive oil,
for frying

Wash courgettes, grate them and place into a colander with 1 tbsp salt to drain completely. For better results, place grated courgettes in a piece of cloth and squeeze off all liquid. In a large bowl, mix courgettes, parsley, onions, beaten eggs, cheese, pepper and toasted bread. Knead well until the mixture is as thick as a paste, adding more bread if needed. Heat olive oil in a frying pan. Take heaping table-spoons of the mixture, shape into patties, dredge with flour and fry on both sides until golden brown. Dry on kitchen roll and serve.

Tomato pancakes

3 tomatoes, finely chopped
1 grated medium onion
1 teaspoon salt
½ teaspoon pepper
1 teaspoon oregano
1 tbsp parsley or mint, finely chopped
1 cup self-rising flour
olive oil for frying

In a large bowl, put onion, tomatoes, oregano, parsley or mint, salt and freshly ground pepper. Add flour and knead until the ingredients are well combined and have the consistency of a thick batter. Heat olive oil in a frying pan and when it's ready take tablespoons of the batter and drop carefully into the pan. Fry on both sides until golden brown. Dry on kitchen roll and serve immediately.
One egg, 3 tbsp cheese and one more tbsp flour can be added to the batter, if desired.

Spinach pancakes

1 kg spinach
2 medium dried onions or 5-6 spring onions
½ cup finely chopped dill
½ cup finely chopped parsley

salt and pepper
1 cup self-rising flour, olive oil for frying

Wash spinach and put it in boiling water for 5 minutes. Drain and chop it finely. In a large bowl, mix spinach, onions, dill, parsley, salt and pepper. Make a thick batter with 1 cup flour and 1 cup water and add to the mixture. Combine well, adding a little more salt, if needed. Heat olive oil in a frying pan and put in tablespoons of the spinach mixture. Fry on both sides until golden brown. Dry on kitchen roll.

Scrambled eggs

2 finely chopped green peppers
2 finely chopped onions, 3 grated ripe tomatoes
5 eggs
½ cup crumbled feta cheese or any other cheese
1 teaspoon oregano, salt and pepper
4 tbsp olive oil

Heat olive oil in a skillet over medium heat and soften onions and peppers. Add tomatoes and simmer until almost all liquid has evaporated, stirring occasionally. Break

the eggs and put into the skillet one at a time stirring with a wooden spoon until they are cooked and combined with the rest of the ingredients in the skillet.
Add cheese, salt, pepper and oregano and cook for a further 5 minutes, stirring often until liquid is cooked off. Serve warm.

Fried mussels

1 kg mussels
olive oil, for frying
❖ ***For the batter:*** ½ cup flour

1 egg
1 teaspoon salt, ½ teaspoon baking soda
1 cup beer or water
❖ ***For the yoghurt dip:*** 300 grams strained yoghurt
3 mashed garlic cloves
2 tbsp vinegar or lemon juice
2 tbsp olive oil
salt, pepper, ½ cup roughly ground walnuts

First prepare the yoghurt dip by combining yoghurt, garlic, salt, pepper, olive oil, vinegar or lemon juice and walnuts.
Prepare the mussels: Wash and remove the hairy edges.

Boil them in a large pot with enough water for 5 minutes until the mussels have opened. Discard those which have not opened, as they are dead. Separate the mussels from their shells and sprinkle with salt and pepper.
Make a thick batter with the beer or water, beaten egg, salt, baking soda and flour.
Dip mussels, one at a time, in the batter and fry in very hot olive oil until golden brown on both sides. Drain on kitchen roll. Place on a serving tray with yoghurt dip in the centre.

Eggs with tomato sauce

1 medium-size onion, finely chopped
1 bell pepper, finely chopped
2 tbsp olive oil
2 tomatoes, peeled, seeded and chopped
salt, pepper
2 tbsp grated cheese (optional)
2 eggs

Fry onion and pepper in olive oil until soft. Add tomatoes, salt and pepper and when the sauce thickens, stir in cheese.
Break the eggs in the sauce, sprinkle with a little salt and fry until the egg whites are cooked.

ONLY OLIVE OIL IN SALADS

Extra virgin olive oil, the natural juice of the olive, is the oil which should never be left out of salads. On Crete, an area with a high production of olive oil, salads swim -well almost- in olive oil and this seems strange to visitors who are not used to this.
Extra virgin olive oil offers the chance of extremely healthy combinations, especially when the salads use fresh vegetables and greens, as is used in the traditional Greek diet. Again, it is Crete that gives a true example for life.
The Cretans prefer to eat their own fresh vegetables and the bountiful greens which the earth produces unaided, without being cooked. In nearly all the traditional salads there is the combination of extra virgin olive oil with various greens and vegetables.

Greek salad with olives

2 firm tomatoes, 2 cucumbers, ½ cup purslane,
1 medium-size onion, ½ cup parsley
1 green pepper, 1 tbsp pickled capers
5-6 black olives, ½ teaspoon salt
100 grams feta cheese, 1 teaspoon oregano
4 tbsp olive oil, 1 tbsp vinegar

Wash tomatoes, cucumbers, parsley, green pepper and purslane. Cut all of them into pieces and put in a salad bowl. Add capers, onion cut into thin rings and olives. Season with salt and oregano, pour over the dressing with olive oil and vinegar and mix. At the end place feta cheese on top of the salad.

Greek salad with dried rusks

On Crete they are used to eating dried rusks, bread which had been in the oven (for quite a few hours at very low temperature) for a second time and had been dried out. In the old days, this was the easiest way of preserving bread by the farmers as it wasn't possible to cook fresh bread every day. Many types of dried rusks in various shapes can be found in Greece, whether rectangular, square or circular and also dried rusks made with a range of ingredients and with different ways of preparation (rusks made with whole wheat, with barley flour, with a mixture of wheat and barley, with chick peas etc.). These rusks are hard, thick, toasted slices of bread which are softened with water or olive oil and then eaten. Shops in Europe and America which sell Greek products have these dried rusks and the best are from Crete.

For this salad use the same ingredients as for the above salad, but first place 2 rusks in the salad bowl, broken in chunks and drizzled with 2 tablespoons olive oil.

Salad with greens

2 cups greens (chicory, rocket, lettuce, saw thistles)
1 finely chopped spring onion
salt
3 tbsp olive oil
1 tbsp vinegar or lemon juice
1 tbsp pomegranate seeds (optional)

Wash greens, chop them and place in a salad bowl together with the onion.
Whisk olive oil with salt and vinegar or lemon juice and pour over the salad. Toss gently, add pomegranate seeds and serve.

Salad with rocket and tomatoes

2 firm tomatoes, cut into wedges
1 cup roughly chopped rocket
10 olives

½ teaspoon salt pepper
3 tbsp olive oil
1 tbsp vinegar

Place in a salad bowl the tomatoes, rocket and olives. Make a dressing by shaking well olive oil, vinegar, salt and pepper and pour over the salad.

Salad with apples and walnuts

1 cup grated carrot
1 cup grated cabbage
1 cup grated beetroot
1 cup grated apple
½ cup roughly ground walnuts
5 tbsp olive oil
3 tbsp lemon juice or vinegar
salt, pepper

In a salad bowl mix vegetables, apple and walnuts. Shake olive oil, vinegar, salt and pepper until well combined and pour the dressing over the salad.

Purslane with yoghurt and walnuts

Purslane is a self-sown plant in many countries, but usually it is regarded as a weed in gardens. On Crete, which has given many lessons on a healthy diet, purslane is not considered a weed. On the contrary, it is cultivated, as it is eaten regularly in salads. You can grow purslane even in plant pots where it will thrive for years! Purslane has a large quantity of Omega 3 fats, which is believed to be a shield of protection for the heart.

½ kg purslane
3 tbsp olive oil
250 grams strained yoghurt
2 mashed garlic cloves
1 tbsp vinegar or lemon juice
½ teaspoon salt
2 tbsp roughly chopped walnuts

Wash and clean purslane, discarding the thick sprigs. Put it in a salad bowl. Combine well yoghurt with garlic, olive oil, vinegar or lemon juice, salt and walnuts. Pour over purslane and mix.

Dried bean salad

1 cup dried beans
1 medium onion cut into slices
2 green peppers cut into slices
3 tomatoes, seeded and chopped
3 tbsp finely chopped parsley
1 tbsp finely chopped basil (optional)
4 tbsp olive oil
2 tbsp vinegar or lemon juice
salt
10 black olives
2 boiled eggs (optional)

Boil the beans in water until soft but not overcooked and then drain. (They can be soaked in water for a few hours prior to cooking).

In a salad bowl, mix beans with onion, peppers, tomatoes and parsley. Whisk olive oil with salt and vinegar or lemon juice and pour over the salad. Garnish with olives and slices of boiled eggs.

The salad is quite delicious if you just add finely chopped onion and dill and a dressing with olive oil and lemon juice.

Bulgur salad

1 cup bulgur (wheat which has been boiled and then ground)
1 finely chopped dried onion or 5-6 spring onions
2 tomatoes, seeded and chopped

2 tbsp finely chopped parsley
1 tbsp finely chopped mint (optional)
4 tbsp olive oil
2 tbsp vinegar
salt, ½ mashed hot pepper

Soak bulgur in warm water for one hour and drain well. Add remaining ingredients and mix well.

OLIVE OIL IN PULSES

In the traditional diet of Crete, pulses play a leading role, one which is detected in the finds of archaeological and palaeobotanic researches. Since prehistoric times, the inhabitants of Crete but also the Aegean in general have used pulses on a regular basis in their diet. Panspermia, the offering to the gods of a small amount of all the grains, was an important expression of thanks by the ancient Greeks but also a ritual ceremony for vegetation and renewal of life.

Greek mythology has documented the importance of pulses as ritual dishes, stating that this was Deucalion and Pyrrha's first food after the flood which destroyed mankind.

When the downpour stopped and the floods ebbed, the two mythological founders of mankind were to be found on earth alone and without food. The only thing that had remained was a few seeds of all kinds. They boiled these altogether and ate them with mixed feelings. On the one hand, they felt the joy of being saved and on the other, the great loss of all the other people. It really was a meal of great joy and sorrow all mixed up! If we look again at the symbolism in this myth, then we will see that the circle of joy and sorrow is one and the same with the circle of life as it is with the seed: we bury it but it does not die, instead, it is reborn, growing and producing other seeds in the process!

In the nutritional culture, pulses are almost always consumed with olive oil. There are days when the Orthodox Church disallows the consumption of olive oil, but pulses, soaked in water for a few hours, are still eaten. These pulses are eaten with olives! "Vrechtokoukia" (broad beans which have been left a whole day in water to dampen and soften) are perfect and they are a main dish in Lent foods on Crete and the Aegean islands. In periods of religious fasting, in some monasteries they are used to cooking pulses with olives.

The science of nutrition heavily recommends that today, people should not abandon this food which has been so important for both the development of society and the maintenance of good health, as has happened in many western societies.

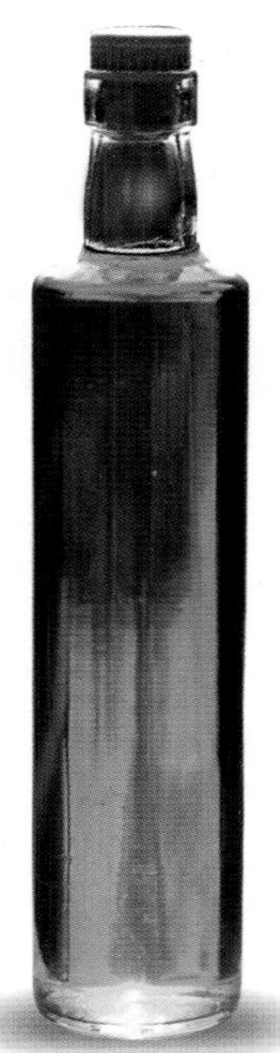

Of course, it is recommended that these dishes should be eaten with olive oil! Olive oil, apart from offering a unique guarantee of health, completes the dishes which are prepared with pulses and produces a harmony of tastes. Traditional cooking offers various suggestions on the making of dishes based on pulses, such as pulses with vegetables or mashed pulses.

Split pea purée

Mediterranean fava is made with broad beans. Greek fava uses peeled and cracked seeds of the plant Lathyrus Sativus (yellow lentil). In other countries fava is usually to be found in Greek speciality shops. The dish which is made in the Greek way resembles a purée and is drizzled generously with extra virgin olive oil.

½ kg fava (yellow or green split peas)

2 medium onions, roughly chopped
1 teaspoon salt, pepper
3 tbsp olive oil
❖ ***To serve:*** olive oil, according to taste
2 lemons in slices
1 finely chopped onion, olives (optional)

Place split peas in a pot with onion, salt, 3 tbsp olive oil and cover with 5 cups water. Cook over low heat until it becomes a mash and nearly all the water has been boiled off, about one

hour. The pot should not be covered because the fava expands and so it might spill over. Near the end, stir continuously so that it doesn't stick to the bottom of the pot and also to help it turn into a pulp. When it cools, it becomes thicker.
On serving, add olive oil according to taste, finely chopped onion, lemon slices, olives, capers or mint leaves, if so desired. The dish in which fava is served should first be rubbed with garlic.

Mixed pulses (Pallikaria or polysporia)

A traditional dish known throughout nearly all of Greece. In the old days it was made on special occasions (the celebration of the Virgin Mary on 21st November, St Andrew on 30th November etc). Farmers believed that with this dish they helped the good production of cereal crops. It is a survival of ancient Greek customs and, more precisely, of "Thargilia". Then, they boiled crop produce in a pot and offered to the gods. Today in Greece, it is a tasty salad but also a delicious and wholesome soup.

100 grams of each type of pulses (wheat, chick peas, beans, broad beans, lentils etc)
salt, pepper
❖ ***To serve:*** **fresh or dried onion dill, olive oil, lemon juice**

Soak the pulses the night before. Wheat and chickpeas need more time in cooking, therefore place in separate bowls.
Lentils do not need to be soaked at all. The next day, rinse the pulses and place wheat first in a large pot. Cover with enough water and boil for 20 minutes. Add chick peas and cook for another 20 minutes. Add remaining pulses and

continue cooking until soft. Season with salt and pepper and serve either as a soup in its own juices or drained as a salad, in both cases drizzled with olive oil and lemon juice and sprinkled with finely chopped onion and dill, to desired taste.

Lentil soup

½ kg lentils (brown)
1 medium onion finely chopped
½ cup olive oil
2-3 finely chopped garlic cloves
1 tbsp tomato paste or 3 ripe grated tomatoes
3 bay leaves, salt, pepper
2 tbsp good quality vinegar

Place lentils in a pot with enough water to cover them and boil for 5-6 minutes., then drain them. Brown onion in olive oil, add the lentils, garlic, tomato paste diluted in 1 cup water or just the tomatoes, bay leaves, salt, pepper and water to cover. Boil the lentils until cooked which will take about half an hour. Add vinegar, boil for 5 more minutes and the dish is ready.

Boiled dried broad beans

½ kilo dried broad beans
1 grated onion
½ kilo grated tomatoes
½ cup olive oil
salt

Soak broad beans in water overnight. The following day remove the black tips and most husks from the beans and then put them in a pot with enough water to cover them (about 1,5 litre). Boil the beans until almost done, add onion, tomatoes, olive oil and salt and continue boiling until most water has been absorbed. Towards the end, stir often so that they don't stick to the bottom of the pot.
Serve the beans drizzled with olive oil and sprinkled with finely chopped onion and oregano.

Black-eyed beans with fennel

½ kg black-eyed beans
½ cup olive oil
1 medium onion, finely chopped
300 grams finely chopped fennel

1 tbsp tomato paste or ½ kg grated tomatoes
salt and pepper, to taste

Put the beans in a pot, cover well with water and boil for half an hour to half-cook. Transfer the beans into a colander to drain. Put olive oil, onion and fennel in the pot and sauté for 5 minutes. Add 2-3 cups water and cook for 15 minutes, then add tomato paste diluted in 1 cup water or the tomatoes, salt and pepper. Allow fennel to slowly simmer and almost cook, at which point add the beans, along with more water to cover and leave to cook completely.

Spaniatha

Basic but special food with Byzantine roots. Byzantine texts refer to "aghiozoumi", holy juice from water, oil and aromatic plants, which were boiled together and served on plates, poured over slices of bread which had been placed on them. From this dish, come various country dishes which are still made in Greece, such as "panatha", a simple and basic meal. "Spaniatha" is linked to the Asterousia, the mountains in southern Crete and shows a different version of the Byzantine dish.

300 grams dried beans
5 tbsp olive oil
1 medium onion in slices
salt, pepper, dried rusks

In a pot with enough water, boil the beans until cooked, making sure that some juice is left. Brown the onion in olive oil in a pan until it changes colour. Add beans with their juice, salt and pepper and cook for 10 minutes.
Serve in a dish with a dried rusk underneath the beans. (It is optional to add lemon juice).

Chickpeas with spinach

300 grams chickpeas
1 kilo coarsely chopped spinach
½ cup olive oil, 1 finely chopped onion
½ kilo grated tomatoes
salt, pepper

Right: Spaniatha

Soak chickpeas in water the evening before. The following day heat olive oil in a pot and sauté onion until translucent. Add chickpeas, cover with water and cook for about one hour until almost done. Pour in the tomato, spinach, salt and pepper and cook for another 20-25 minutes.

Chick pea balls

½ kg chick peas
1 grated medium-sized onion
2 egg yolks, 4 tbsp of ground dried rusk or toasted bread
½ cup finely chopped parsley
salt, pepper
½ cup grated cheese (optional)
flour, olive foil for frying

Soak chick peas overnight and the next day drain and rub them to remove husks. Rinse with cold water and then boil them in a pot until soft. Drain again and place in a food processor along with 2-3 tbsp of the water from boiling. Grind for 2-3 minutes, add the other ingredients and grind to combine them well. Taking a tablespoon of mixture at a time, shape into croquettes. Dredge with flour and fry them in olive oil. Serve alone or with tomato sauce.
In the same way you can make croquettes with split peas or with different pulses together (dried beans, broad beans, chick peas and split peas).

PASTAS AND OLIVE OIL

Mussels pilaf

1 kg mussels, 2 cups rice
4-5 tbsp olive oil
2 medium onions, finely chopped
100 ml white wine
2 medium tomatoes, seeded and mashed
salt and pepper to taste

Prepare the mussels: Wash and scrub them very well and remove the hairy edges. Boil them in a large pot with enough water for 5 minutes until the mussels have opened. Discard those which have not opened, as they are dead. Separate the mussels from their shells and leave them aside. Heat oil in a pot and soften onions for 3-4 minutes. Add mussels and, after a while, the rice and stir for another 4 minutes. Pour in wine, tomatoes and 5 cups water and keep cooking over medium heat until almost all liquid has been absorbed, about 15 minutes. Season with salt and pepper, stir for another minute and remove from heat. Cover with a clean towel until served.

Stuffed Courgette Flowers

40 courgette flowers, ½ kg mashed tomatoes
2 onions, finely chopped
2 tbsp parsley, finely chopped
½ kg rice, salt and pepper to taste
3/4 cup olive oil

Buy or pick the courgette flowers in the morning when they are wide open. Place them upright in a bowl to keep them open until you need them. When you are ready, wash them carefully because they tear easily. Prepare the stuffing: In a large bowl mix rice, onions, ½ cup olive oil, tomatoes, parsley, 1 cup water, salt and pepper. (You can substitute half the rice to the same quantity of minced meat). Pour remaining oil in a pot. Take one courgette flower at a time and carefully fill with 1 tbsp rice stuffing. Fold the top of the flower over to close it and place each flower in the pot. Place a plate over the "dolmathes" to keep them from opening, pour enough water to almost cover them and simmer for about 40 minutes, until almost all liquid has been absorbed.

Ground wheat pilaf with tomato sauce

½ kg chondros or bulgur ***(chondros is roughly ground wheat while bulgur is wheat which has been first boiled and then ground)***
½ cup olive oil, 2 medium onions, finely chopped
2 courgettes, finely chopped, 1 potato, finely chopped
½ kg finelly chopped tomatoes
salt and pepper to taste

Wash and drain chondros or bulgur: Put it in a large bowl with hot water to cover it, add 2 tbsp salt and when water gets cold place chondros or bulgur in a colander and rinse it thoroughly. In a pot heat olive oil and soften onions until translucent.

Add courgettes, potato and tomatoes and stir for 5 minutes. Pour 6 cups water or meat stock and when it comes to the boil, add the chondros or bulgur. (The ratio of water to bulgur should be 2,5:1). Reduce heat to low and simmer until the water is absorbed and the bulgur soft, about 20 minutes, stirring often to prevent it from sticking to the bottom of the pot. Serve sprinkled with grated cheese, if desired.

Spaghetti with garlic

½ kilo spaghetti
7-8 mashed garlic cloves
5-6 tbsp olive oil
½ kilo finely chopped tomatoes
salt, pepper, 1 cup grated cheese

Boil spaghetti in ample salted water, taking care not to overcook it, and put into a sieve.
In the meantime prepare the sauce: heat olive oil in a pan, add garlic, tomatoes, salt and pepper and cook until the sauce thickens. Serve spaghetti with the garlic sauce on top. Sprinkle with the cheese.

Artichoke pilaf

5 artichoke hearts cut into cubes
3-4 tbsp olive oil
5-6 spring onions, finely chopped
3 medium-size carrots, cut into cubes
3 tbsp finely chopped dill, 1 cup rice
salt and black pepper, juice of 1 lemon

Prepare the artichokes: Remove the leaves and trim them very well leaving only the fleshy middle part, the heart. Rub with lemon and put them aside. Wash and drain rice as above. Heat olive oil in a pot and add spring onions, carrots, artichokes and dill. Stir for 8-10 minutes until juice has evaporated and add rice. Stir a couple of times with a wooden spoon and then pour in 2,5 cups warm water, salt and pepper and cook until liquid has been absorbed. Remove pot from heat, pour in lemon juice, give a good stir and cover pot with a clean towel for a quarter of an hour before the pilaf is served.

MEAT - FISH WITH OLIVE OIL

Chourmouzis – Vyzantius came to Crete from Constantinople at the beginning of 19th century. A phrase expressed by him, "they cook even pork with olive oil", shows the great importance of the precious juice of olives in a unique manner. Various foreign travellers to Crete but also groups of doctors who studied the dietary habits of the Cretans were equally surprised. This fact is almost inconceivable to the inhabitants of northern regions or northern countries because they use animal fat in cooking such dishes. Maybe that was similarly inconceivable to Cretans who ""are used to cooking with olive oil", as the learned British traveller Robert Pashley wrote in 1834.

The American members of the Rockefeller Foundation who carried out a study in 1948, observed the dietary habits of the inhabitants of the island and pointed out that "at noon they eat vegetables, pulses or starches".

On the island of Crete, where the diet of the people is believed to be the healthiest in the world and certainly the model of the Mediterranean diet, meat is consumed usually cooked with wild edible greens, vegetables and pulses. Even the formal Easter dish is lamb or goat with seasonal vegetables (wild greens, lettuce or artichokes...) cooked with olive oil, of course!

Olive oil gives a special taste to meat or fish dishes, makes them lighter and healthier.

Grilled meat with olive oil

1,5 kg meat (any kind of meat)
½ cup olive oil, juice of 2 lemons
1 teaspoon salt, 1 tbsp oregano

Wash meat, cut into serving portions, put in a large bowl and add olive oil, lemon juice, salt and oregano. Let it marinate for at least 4 hours, turning it on all sides to soak in the marinade. Grill the meat on barbecue fire, basting it from time to time with the marinade until soft and brown.

Pork with potatoes and coriander

1 kg boneless pork
4 medium potatoes
4-5 tbsp olive oil
4 cloves of garlic, finely chopped
3/4 cup red wine
2 tbsp coriander
salt and black pepper

Cut meat in cubes, wash and place in a large bowl. Make marinade by combining garlic, wine, coriander, salt and pepper. Pour over meat, cover and put the bowl in a cool place for at least 4 hours. Turn the meat pieces on all sides from time to time to marinate fully. Heat olive oil in a saucepan. Remove meat from marinade with a slotted spoon and put in the pot turning frequently to brown lightly. Add marinade to pot, reduce fire and simmer until half done, adding water if needed. Add potatoes peeled, washed and quartered, a little salt and continue cooking for about half an hour, adding more water again, if needed.

Pork or lamb with prunes

1.5 kg meat (pork or lamb)
1 medium onion, finely chopped
salt, pepper, a little nutmeg
1 cinnamon stick, 5-6 whole cloves
juice of 2 lemons, 3-4 tbsp olive oil
½ kg pitted prunes
½ cup almonds
2 tbsp sugar or honey

Wash meat and cut into cubes. Place it in a large bowl and add onion, salt, pepper, nutmeg, cinnamon, cloves and lemon juice. Allow it to marinate for at least 1 hour.
In the meantime soak prunes in water. Soak almonds in hot water, peel, roast and put aside. Heat olive oil in a large pot, add meat and cook until juice has evaporated. Pour in marinade along with 1-2 cups lukewarm water and simmer until meat is

soft enough, about one hour. Add prunes, almonds and sugar or honey and continue cooking for 10 more minutes. Serve warm.

Veal with spaghetti

1 kg veal
1 large onion, finely chopped
5 tbsp olive oil

3 cloves of garlic, coarsely chopped
100 ml white wine
1 kg finelly chopped tomatoes
1 cinnamon stick, 5-6 cloves
2-3 bay leaves, salt, pepper
½ kg spaghetti No 5
1 cup grated cheese

Wash meat, cut into cubes and dry. In a large pot heat olive oil and add meat. Cook turning on all sides on moderate heat until juice is evaporated. Stir in wine, garlic, tomatoes, cinnamon, cloves, bay leaves, salt, pepper, 1-2 cups water and simmer until meat is soft enough, about one and a half hours. In another large pot put in water, one teaspoon salt and bring to the boil. Add spaghetti and boil for 15 minutes over high heat.

Transfer into a colander and rinse with cold water.

Serve spaghetti topped with meat and sauce and sprinkled with grated cheese.

Chicken in wine

1 medium-size chicken
½ cup olive oil
2 medium onions, finely chopped
3 cloves of garlic, finely chopped
2 cups red wine
½ kg ripe tomatoes, peeled, seeded and chopped
salt and pepper to taste

Cut chicken into serving pieces, wash well and pat dry with kitchen roll. In a large stewing pot, heat olive oil and brown onion for 3 minutes. Continue with meat until juice is evaporated, turning frequently on all sides. Add garlic, wine and 2 cups warm water and simmer till meat is half cooked. Add tomatoes, salt and pepper and continue cooking for another 30 minutes. Serve with plain rice, with roasted or fried potatoes or with noodles.

Baked mackerel with raisins and walnuts

1,5 kg mackerel fish or trout
2 medium onions, finely chopped
2-3 garlic cloves, finely chopped
5 tbsp olive oil
½ kg tomatoes peeled, seeded and chopped
½ cup seedless raisins, soaked in water for 30 minutes
½ cup coarsely ground walnuts, salt, pepper

Clean mackerel, remove guts, season with salt and place in a baking tray in one layer.
Combine tomatoes, onions, garlic, raisins, walnuts, salt and pepper and stuff the fish with this mixture. Spread the rest of the mixture on top of the fish, drizzle with olive oil and bake for 50-60 minutes.

Cod with potatoes in lemon sauce

1 kg salted cod (preferably filleted) or fresh cod
1 kg potatoes, ½ cup olive oil
1 large onion, finely chopped
3 garlic cloves, finely chopped
3 tbsp lemon juice, pepper

Cut cod into serving portions and place in a large bowl filled with cold water. Soak cod for 15-18 hours, changing

the water 3-4 times. When fish is ready, heat olive oil in a large pot and soften onions until they gain a little colour. Add potatoes peeled and cut into quarters, garlic and 2 cups water and simmer for 15 minutes. Place cod on top of the potatoes and cook gently for a further 20 minutes, shaking the pot from time to time. Five minutes before food is ready pour lemon juice over the food and shake the pot. If you prefer a thicker sauce, you can dilute one tbsp of flour in a little water and add it to the pot along with the lemon juice.

Baked fish with vegetables and rosemary

1 big whole fish
(grouper, red snapper, pike, sea bream, mullet)
3-4 sun dried tomatoes
2-3 bay leaves, 3 tbsp finely chopped parsley
3-4 medium onions, sliced into thin rings
2 finely chopped garlic cloves
4 tbsp olive oil, 100 ml white wine
3 medium tomatoes peeled, seeded and chopped
salt, pepper, 1 teaspoon rosemary
½ cup black olives
(optional)

Clean fish, remove guts and stuff with parsley, bay leaves and sun dried tomatoes. Place in an oiled baking tray. In a saucepan heat oil and brown onions lightly. Add garlic, tomatoes, wine, rosemary, olives, salt and pepper and simmer for 5 minutes. Pour the sauce over and around the fish and bake in moderate heat for about an hour.

Bream with celery

1 kg medium size bream fish
1 kg coarsely chopped celery
2 medium onions, finely chopped
½ cup olive oil
salt and pepper
2 eggs, juice of 2 lemons

Clean, gut and wash fish. Season with salt and keep in the fridge. Wash celery and put in large pot with boiling water for 5 minutes. Drain and leave aside.

In a saucepan heat olive oil, brown onions for 3-4 minutes and add celery, salt and pepper. Cover with warm water and simmer for about 25-30 minutes. Place the fish on top of celery and continue simmering for 20 more minutes, without stirring but just shaking the pot from time to time to prevent food from sticking to the bottom of the pot.
When food has been cooked, prepare the egg and lemon sauce: Beat the eggs (first the whites and then the yolks) with the lemon juice until frothy. Add a few ladles of liquid from the pot beating constantly until the egg and lemon mixture is warm. Remove pot from heat, pour in the egg mixture and stir well.

Baked fish with bell peppers

1 big whole fish
(pike, red snapper, mullet, monkfish)
3 tbsp finely chopped parsley
2 medium onions, sliced into thin rings
2 finely chopped garlic cloves
½ kg finely chopped tomatoes
½ kg bell peppers, sliced into rings
6 tbsp olive oil
100 ml white wine
salt, pepper, juice of 1 lemon

Combine onions, peppers, tomatoes and garlic and place in an oiled baking tray.
Clean fish, remove guts, stuff with parsley and place on top of the sauce. Season with salt, drizzle with olive oil, wine and lemon juice and bake in moderate heat for about one hour.

Fish Soup (Kakavia)

This is the favourite soup of the Greek fishermen but also of the inhabitants of the islands and coastal areas of Greece. It can be prepared in various manners, but fishermen used to make it very simply, with only sea water, without, of course, adding any salt. Having its origin in Greek antiquity, it took its name from the pot in which it was cooked in Byzantine years, the "kakavi". The very well known bouillabaisse of Marseilles is believed to have evolved from this Greek fish soup.

1,5 kg whole fish
(bass, cod, red snapper, pike, grouper)
4 tbsp olive oil
2 onions, sliced into thin rings
5-6 medium potatoes, peeled and cut into quarters
salt, pepper, juice of 2 lemons
1,5 litre water

Scrape and wash fish and remove guts. Cut into large slices. In a soup pot heat olive oil and soften onions until lightly brown. Add potatoes and cover with enough water. Boil for 10 minutes, then add fish, salt and pepper and continue cooking for a further 25-30 minutes. Remove pot from heat and pour in lemon juice.

Meat with spinach in tomato sauce

1 kg meat (lamb or veal)
1 kg spinach
6 tbsp olive oil
2 medium onions, finely chopped
½ kg tomatoes peeled, seeded and chopped
salt and pepper to taste

Wash meat and cut into cubes. Heat the oil in a saucepan and soften the onions until they take on a little colour. Add meat and turn a few times on all sides to colour evenly. Stir in tomatoes, one cup water and cook gently for about 50 minutes. In the meantime wash and chop spinach. When meat is almost cooked, stir in spinach, salt and pepper and continue cooking until almost all liquid has been absorbed.

Meat balls with potatoes in the oven

½ kg minced meat (lamb and veal or pork)
1 egg, beaten
2 grated onions, 2 mashed garlic cloves
2 slices of stale bread, soaked in water and squeezed dry, 3 tbsp finely chopped parsley
½ kg tomatoes peeled, seeded and chopped
1 bell pepper, finely chopped
1 teaspoon dried thyme
6 medium potatoes
salt and pepper
4 tbsp olive oil

In a large bowl mix and knead minced meat, 1 onion, garlic, egg, parsley, bell pepper, bread, thyme, salt and pepper punching the mixture with your knuckles.
Peel potatoes, cut into round slices, season with salt and pepper and place in an oiled baking tray.
Take small portions of the minced meat mixture, shape into balls and gently flatten them. Place on top of potatoes.
Heat olive oil in a pan and brown the other onion for 3 minutes. Stir in tomatoes, one cup water, salt and pepper and simmer for 5 minutes. Top with sauce and bake in moderate heat for 25- 30 minutes. Turn meatballs on the other side and continue cooking for another 20 minutes.

Rabbit with walnuts

1 medium-size rabbit
½ cup olive oil
3 onions, sliced into thin rings
½ cup white wine
salt
½ cup coarsely, ground walnuts
❖ ***For the marinade:***
1,5 cup white wine
1 cup celery root sliced into rings
2 carrots sliced into rings
2 cloves of garlic, peeled but whole
1 cinnamon stick
5-6 whole cloves
2-3 bay leaves
2 onions, sliced into thin rings
5-6 peppercorns

Make marinade the evening before by combining the above ingredients. Wash and cut rabbit into serving pieces, place in a large bowl and cover with marinade.
The next day, heat olive oil in a saucepan and soften onions for 2-3 minutes until lightly brown. Remove rabbit pieces from marinade and add to the pan. Brown for 10 minutes until juice is evaporated and stir in ½ cup wine. Add walnuts and salt and simmer until rabbit is tender, about 40-45 minutes.

Roasted lamb with tomato sauce

1 kg lamb
1 kg potatoes, peeled and cut into quarters
½ kg tomatoes, cut into slices
juice of 1 lemon
6 tbsp olive oil
2-3 bay leaves
salt and pepper to taste

Wash meat, cut into serving pieces, dry and baste with lemon juice. Place in a baking tray, season with salt, pepper and 3 tbsp olive oil.

Place potatoes all around meat, season again with salt and pepper, place bay leaves among potatoes and drizzle remaining olive oil.

Top with tomato slices, pour in ½ cup water and bake in moderate heat for about an hour and a half, turning the meat over half way through.

Beef stew

1 kg beef
6 tbsp olive oil
½ kg pearl onions or large onions sliced into thin rings
3 garlic cloves
2 tbsp vinegar
salt, pepper
1 teaspoon pimento
1 cinnamon stick

Wash meat and cut into cubes. Heat olive oil in a saucepan, add meat and cook on medium heat until juice has evaporated. Add onions and peeled whole cloves of garlic and soften for 5 minutes. Stir in vinegar, salt, pepper, pimento, cinnamon and 2-3 cups warm water. Cover and simmer for 2 hours, until meat is tender.

Baked anchovies or sardines with olive oil and oregano

1 kg anchovies or sardines
2 large onions, sliced into thin rings
salt, pepper
4 tbsp olive oil, 5 tbsp lemon juice
1 tbsp oregano

Wash fish, remove heads and guts, season with salt and put into a colander to drain.
Place onions in an oiled baking tray or ovenproof dish and put fish on them. Whisk together olive oil, lemon juice, pepper and oregano and pour over fish. Bake in preheated oven for about 40 minutes, until fish is lightly brown.

Mycenaean stew

In summer 1999 an original exhibition took place in the National Archaeological Museum, Athens. The title was "Minoan and Mycenaean Tastes" and John Tzedakis was the head archaeologist. The researchers displayed items and presented evidence (laboratory analyses) proving the early use of olive oil in cooking by the inhabitants of Minoan Crete, even before 2000 B.C. Among other documents they published a few indicative recipes that might be close to the dietary habits of the Minoan or the Mycenaean Greeks.

1 kg pork
½ cup olive oil
1 kg coarsely chopped onions
2 finely chopped garlic cloves
2 bay leaves, 2 cups wine
salt, pepper, cumin

Wash meat and cut into cubes. Heat olive oil in a stewing pot and lightly brown onions. Add bay leaves, garlic and meat. Cook until juice is evaporated and then pour in wine. Season with salt, pepper, cumin, reduce heat to low and simmer for 2 hours, until meat is tender.

Lamb or kid with yoghurt

1 kg meat (lamb or kid)
½ kg strained yoghurt
4 tbsp olive oil, salt

Wash meat and cut into medium pieces. Place in a saucepan with olive oil and cook on low heat until tender. Top with yoghurt, season with salt and cook for a further 15 minutes.

Dried beans with meat in the oven

1 kg meat (pork, veal or goat)
½ kg dried beans
2 medium onions, finely chopped
4 medium tomatoes, peeled, seeded and chopped
3 slices of sun dried tomatoes
2 finely chopped garlic cloves
½ cup olive oil

½ cup finely chopped parsley
1 chilli pepper (optional)
salt, pepper

In a large pot put beans with enough water to cover them and boil for 10 minutes. Drain the beans. Wash meat, cut into cubes and place in a baking tray. Add beans, onions, tomatoes, garlic, olive oil, parsley, chilli pepper, salt and freshly ground black pepper. Pour one litre water over beans, cover with aluminum foil and bake in moderate heat for about 2 hours. When food is almost ready, uncover the pan and bake for a further 15 minutes.

Meat soup with vegetables

½ kg meat (lamb or veal)
4 tbsp olive oil
2 large onions, sliced into thin rings
2 celery roots sliced into 2 cm rings
2 leeks, sliced into rings
2 medium carrots, cut into cubes
3-4 medium potatoes, cut into cubes
salt

Wash meat and cut into small cubes. Put in a soup pot with water to cover it. Add salt and bring to a slow boil skimming foam off top from time to time. Simmer until meat is almost ready. In another saucepan heat olive oil, soften onions until they get a little colour and add celery, leeks, carrots and finally potatoes, stirring for 10-15 minutes. Season with salt and transfer into the pot with meat, add some more water if it is not enough, and continue cooking for another 15-20 minutes.

Lamb and artichokes in egg-lemon sauce

1 kg lamb, ½ cup olive oil
3-4 spring onions, coarsely chopped
½ cup finely chopped dill
1 kg artichoke hearts
salt, pepper
2 eggs, 2 lemons

Prepare the artichokes: Remove the leaves and trim them very well leaving only the fleshy middle part, the heart. Rub with lemon and put aside. Wash meat and cut into pieces removing as much fat as you can.

Heat olive oil in a large pot, put in meat and brown on all sides for a few minutes. Add onion, dill, salt and pepper and 2 cups warm water. Simmer for about 40 minutes and then put in the artichokes. Cook for another 35 to 40 minutes adding more water if necessary. Once the meat is done, prepare the egg and lemon sauce (avgolemono):
Beat the eggs (first the whites and then the yolks) with the lemon juice until frothy. Add a few ladles of the stock from the pot, beating constantly until the egg and lemon mixture is warm. Remove pot from heat, pour in the egg mixture and shake the pot to mix the egg-lemon mixture with the food.

Chicken with parsley in egg-lemon sauce

1 medium-size chicken
1 kg parsley
5-6 tbsp olive oil
5-6 spring onions coarsely chopped
salt, pepper
2 eggs, juice of 2 lemons

Wash parsley and chop it coarsely. Wash chicken and cut into medium pieces. Heat olive oil in a saucepan and brown onions lightly. Add chicken and brown on all sides for 6-7 minutes. Put in parsley along with 3 cups water and cook for about one hour.
When food is ready, season with salt and pepper and prepare the egg and lemon sauce as above.
This recipe is also made with dill in place of parsley.

OLIVE OIL IN PIES

Pies are typical in the cuisine of northern Greece, but as olive oil is neither produced there nor cheap enough to buy, other fat substances are used in their preparation instead of that precious juice from olives. In southern Greece (and especially in the islands) pies are prepared almost exclusively with olive oil. However, the traditional pies of northern areas of Greece can very well be prepared with olive oil.

Pies are a staple among the immigrating population of northern Greece, the Sarakatsans, who used to cook them almost every day. They were the easiest solution for them as they could be prepared with the products they had ready at hand. Olive oil affects the quality of these dishes greatly and this is why the Sarakatsans themselves prefer to buy and use it in their pies.

The pies suggested in this chapter are made with many different ingredients. Some of them, though, are very interesting, such as the olive oil pie (lathenia), which is traditional in the cuisine of some small islands in the Cyclades. The name alone shows the importance of olive oil in its preparation.

Cheese pie with olive oil

❖ ***For the puff pastry:*** 1 egg
3 tbsp olive oil, ½ teaspoon salt
1 cup flour, 4-5 tbsp milk
❖ ***For the filling:*** 3 eggs
½ kg feta cheese, crumbled
½ cup milk, 4 tbsp olive oil
3-4 tbsp fine semolina

Prepare a dough with the ingredients for the pastry, cover and refrigerate for 30 minutes. (You can also use commercial pastry). *Prepare the filling:* In a medium-size bowl combine feta cheese, beaten eggs, milk, olive oil and semolina. Blend very well with a fork and refrigerate for 1 hour. Remove dough from refrigerator and roll it out on a lightly floured surface to a circle, the size of a baking tray. Spread the puff pastry on the bottom of an oiled baking tray and place the filling on top. Baste gently with 1-2 beaten eggs and bake in moderate heat until golden brown, for about one hour. After it has cooled a little, cut into pieces and serve.

Olive oil pie (Lathenia)

1,5 cup water
1,5 packet active dry yeast
½ teaspoon salt
½ cup olive oil
800 grams flour
(preferably wheat)
1 medium onion, grated
2-3 finely chopped tomatoes
1 teaspoon dried oregano
100 grams feta cheese,
crumbled (optional)

Dilute yeast in warm water, add half olive oil, salt and flour, a little at a time till you have soft dough. Place the dough in the center of an oiled baking pan and spread all over the bottom of the pan with your oiled finger tips.
Leave it in a warm place to rise until double in bulk and top with onion, tomato, oregano, (feta cheese) and remaining olive oil. Bake in moderate heat for about 50 minutes.

Spinach-and-greens pie

❖***For the filling:*** 1 kg greens finely chopped
5-6 spring onions, finely chopped
½ cup dill, finely chopped, ½ cup fennel, finely chopped
½ cup olive oil, salt and pepper
½ cup ground toasted bread
200 grams crumbled feta cheese
❖***For the dough:*** ½ cup water
½ cup olive oil
grated rind and juice of
1 lemon
½ teaspoon salt, 3 cups
self-raising flour

Prepare the dough with the above

ingredients and refrigerate for 30 minutes.
Wash and finely chop spinach and greens. Heat olive oil in a saucepan and soften greens on low heat for about 15 minutes. Drain completely and combine with a little salt, pepper, to desired taste, feta cheese and toasted bread crumbs.
Remove dough from refrigerator and divide into 2 balls, one a little bigger than the other one. Roll out the bigger part on a lightly floured surface into a circle, large enough to fit into the bottom of the pan and hang over its sides by about 2 cms. Place it carefully in oiled pan.
Spread filling evenly on top. Roll out second dough ball into a circle the size of the pan and cover the filling. Bring dough hanging over the outer sides and inner sides of the pan together and pinch carefully to joint them. Baste with olive oil, mark pieces with a sharp knife and bake in moderate heat until golden brown, about one hour.
Cool for at least 20 minutes before serving.

Rice pie

½ kg rice, 8 eggs, 400 grams grated cheese
½ cup olive oil, ½ kg commercial pastry

Put enough water in a large pot, bring to a boil and cook rice for 5 minutes. Place rice in a colander, rinse with cold water under the tap and allow it to drain well. Combine with beaten eggs, salt, cheese and 3 tbsp olive oil.
Layer 3 pastry sheets in an oiled baking tray, one at a time, brushing each one with olive oil. Spread about one third of the filling over the last sheet. Repeat twice and finish by placing 4 pastry sheets on top, brushed again with olive oil. Cut into serving portions with a sharp knife and bake in preheated oven (180° C.) till golden brown, about 1 hour.

Courgette pie

❖ ***For the filling:*** **1 kg courgettes**
1 teaspoon salt, 4 tbsp olive oil
1 medium onion, grated, 1 green pepper, grated
½ cup finely chopped dill or mint
4 eggs, ½ cup grated cheese
½ cup ground toasted bread
❖ ***For the phyllo paste:*** **½ cup olive oil**
½ cup milk, ½ teaspoon salt, ½ kg self-raising flour

Grate courgettes the evening before, season with salt, put into a colander and allow them to drain very well. The following day, combine well with the rest of the ingredients

and leave aside. Prepare the dough for the phyllo: Beat olive oil, milk and salt and slowly add flour until you have soft dough. Divide into 2 balls, one a little bigger than the other one. This you roll out and place on the bottom of an oiled pan leaving 2 cm dough hanging over the sides, as in the above recipe. Spread courgette mixture on top and cover with another phyllo, which you make by rolling out the remaining dough. Bring the dough hanging over the outer sides and inner sides of the pan together and pinch carefully to joint them. Baste with beaten egg, mark pieces with a sharp knife and bake in moderate heat until golden brown, about one hour.

Cheese bread

3 tbsp olive oil
1 cup water
250 grams crumbled feta cheese
1 package dry yeast
½ kg flour

Dilute yeast in lukewarm water and add olive oil and flour little by little until you have soft dough which doesn't stick to the hands. Add feta cheese and knead to combine it with the dough. Place in an oiled bread pan, press with your finger tips and leave it rise until double in bulk. In the meantime preheat oven to 180 C. Baste cheese bread with an egg beaten with a little olive oil and bake in moderate heat for 30-40 minutes.

Baked cheese pasties

❖ ***For the puff pastry:*** **½ cup yoghurt**
½ teaspoon baking soda, ½ cup olive oil
½ teaspoon salt, juice of 1 orange
½ kg flour
❖ ***For the filling:*** **1 egg**
350 grams crumbled feta cheese

Prepare the dough: Beat olive oil with yoghurt, add baking soda diluted in orange juice, salt and flour little by little until you achieve soft and elastic dough. Combine feta cheese and egg for the filling. Take pieces of dough the size of a walnut and roll each one out into a small circle. Place 1 teaspoon filling on one half and cover with the other half. Press the edges down with a fork to close firmly, baste with beaten egg white and bake in moderate heat until golden brown, about 25 minutes.

VEGETABLES AND OLIVE OIL

The Orthodox Church diet requires the consumption of great amounts of vegetables, as they are among the products which are allowed during the fasting periods. Thus, as time passed, a special dietary code was created which goes together with the rural as well as with the older customs. The consumption of vegetables almost always coincides with the consumption of olive oil. In Crete, which, as mentioned above, is considered to be a peak area for the Mediterranean diet, the consumption of vegetables is almost on an everyday basis. This, of course, doesn't suggest dietary monotony, but resourcefulness and inventiveness for unlimited food combinations. This happens because the Cretans do not consume only one (or just a few) kinds of vegetables. Their diet includes an incredible variety of vegetables which go very well with other food products.

Roasted potatoes with olive oil and oregano

1,5 kg potatoes, ½ cup olive oil
1 teaspoon salt, pepper
2 teaspoons dried oregano, juice of 2 lemons

Peel potatoes, cut lengthwise into 4 or more pieces and place in a baking tray. Sprinkle with salt, pepper, oregano, olive oil, lemon juice and 1 cup water. Bake in the oven, first in high temperature for 20 minutes and then in moderate heat for another 50 minutes until the potatoes are soft and golden brown.

Potato purée with olive oil

1 kg potatoes
3/4 cup olive oil *(preferably flavoured with thyme)*
3/4 cup milk
1 teaspoon salt, freshly ground pepper
3/4 cup grated kefalotyri cheese
(hard cheese made from sheep's milk)

Boil potatoes, peel and mash in food processor. Slowly add olive oil, milk, salt, pepper and cheese and continue puréeing until the mixture is smooth.

Fried red peppers with yoghurt sauce

10 red peppers (peppers of Florina)
2 cloves of garlic, 1 teaspoon salt
300 grams strained yoghurt
3 tbsp olive oil
1 tbsp vinegar

Wash peppers, remove stems and seeds, pat dry with kitchen roll and fry or grill until their skin begins to blister.

Mash garlic with salt and mix with yoghurt. Add olive oil and vinegar and combine all ingredients together. Top red peppers with this sauce and serve.

Aubergines stuffed with minced meat

6 large aubergines
6 tbsp olive oil
1 onion, coarsely chopped
250 grams minced meat (lamb and veal)
3 mashed garlic cloves
3-4 tbsp almonds, coarsely ground
4 medium tomatoes, peeled, seeded and chopped
salt and pepper
½ teaspoon ground cinnamon
1 tbsp parsley, finely chopped
1 tbsp fresh mint, finely chopped
1 green pepper and 1 tomato

Wash aubergines, cut off their stems and make an incision lengthwise in each aubergine, being careful not to cut them through. Sprinkle with salt into the incisions and let them stand for 1-2 hours.

In a bowl combine well all the ingredients for the filling: minced meat, onion, garlic, almonds, tomatoes, 2 tbsp olive oil, salt, pepper, cinnamon, parsley and mint.

Drain aubergines and fry slightly on all sides. Place in a baking tray. Taking one aubergine at a time, carefully fill each slit with the minced meat mixture. Cut tomato and pepper into 6 slices each and put the slices on the aubergines. Pour over 4 tbsp olive oil and 4 tbsp water, cover the baking tray with aluminum foil and bake in moderate heat for half an hour. Remove the foil and bake for another 30 minutes.

Peppers stuffed with cheese

1 kg green long peppers
4 tbsp olive oil
1 onion, finely chopped
1 tbsp parsley, finely chopped
½ cup crumbled feta cheese
½ cup grated kefalotyri
(hard cheese made from sheep's milk)
1 teaspoon tomato paste diluted in ½ cup water
pepper to taste

Wash peppers, remove stems and seeds and boil in water for 5 minutes. Drain completely and let them cool down. Heat olive oil in a saucepan, brown the onion and add tomato paste, parsley, feta cheese, kefalotyri cheese and pepper. Simmer for 5 minutes and remove from heat.

Stuff peppers carefully with the mixture, put a chunk of bread in the opening and place them in a baking tray. Baste with a little olive oil and bake in preheated oven for about 40 minutes.

Alternatively, you can fry them.

Eggplants with tomato sauce

2 large aubergines
3-4 medium-size potatoes
½ kg tomatoes, peeled, seeded and chopped
1 medium onion, finely chopped
salt, pepper
cumin, oregano
150 grams crumbled feta cheese
1 cup olive oil for frying

Cut aubergines lengthwise into large oval slices and put in salted water for about one hour.
Slice the potatoes like the aubergines and fry until lightly brown. Drain on kitchen roll, place on a plate and season with salt.
Drain aubergines completely, fry and drain again on kitchen roll. Place on top of potatoes and salt them, too.
Heat a little water in a pan and cook onion in it until it is soft. When water is absorbed, add olive oil, tomatoes, very little salt, pepper, cumin and oregano. Cook until the sauce thickens and then pour it over the potatoes and the eggplants. Sprinkle with crumbled feta cheese, if desired, and serve. This dish is equally delicious when it is cold.

Kritharokouloura (Rusks) with tomato and olive oil

About rusks, those coarse, toasted thick slices of bread, see more in the chapter about salads. The rusks used for this dish are usually round and made from barley or barley and wheat. Rusks seasoned with tomato and olive oil are very popular in Crete, but recently they've become popular in other parts of Greece, too.

2 thick barley or whole wheat paximathia (rusks)
2 ripe tomatoes, peeled, seeded and chopped
2 tbsp olive oil, salt, oregano
100 grams crumbled feta cheese

Sprinkle rusks with very little water to dampen and soften slightly. Place each one on a plate, drizzle tomato, salt, olive oil, oregano and feta cheese and serve immediately. Alternatively you can break the rusk into chunks.

OLIVE OIL IN SWEETS

Even today, visitors to Crete are surprised when they realize that olive oil is used even in the preparation of sweets! Furthermore, in older times, when sugar was imported, therefore expensive, the only sweeteners used by Cretan housewives were vine-juice syrup and honey! Traditional sweets are prepared almost exclusively with olive oil. Some people use refined olive oil to avoid the strong taste. We believe that, in sweets, too, an extra virgin olive oil is required, without a particularly characteristic taste or smell.

New Year's Cake with olive oil

New Year's cake or Saint Basil's cake is the symbol of the Greek New Year's meal. It is either a cake, pie or bread prepared almost all over Greece, although in various ways. A coin is inserted before baking, and whoever finds it in his/her slice is supposed to have good luck in the coming year. It is a survival of the sacred bread of Greek antiquity. Ancient Greeks used to offer such bread to the gods on great feast days. Later, during Roman Saturnalia (Greek celebrations in honour of Cronus), they cast lots to elect the "King of the celebration".

New Year's cake is cut by the head of the family and the first slice is for Christ, the second for the Virgin Mary, the third for Saint Basil, whose feast is on 1st January, and then there follow slices for the household and the members of the family.

1 cup olive oil
1½ cups sugar, 6 eggs
½ teaspoon vanilla extract or 50 ml brandy
grated rind and juice of 2 medium oranges
½ cup milk, ½ kg self-raising flour

Preheat oven to 180° C. Beat olive oil with sugar and continue with yolks, vanilla or brandy, orange rind, orange juice, milk, flour and finally the egg whites beaten stiff. Combine carefully and pour the mixture into an oiled No 30 baking tin. Do not forget to insert a coin.
Bake in preheated oven (180° C) for about 50 minutes without opening the oven door, at least during the first 30 minutes.

Baklavas with olive oil

A very popular Greek sweet which seems to have its roots in ancient Greek gastronomy, when they used to wrap various ingredients in puff pastry and prepare sweets. Such a sweet was "Gastrin", which was mentioned by Athenaeus, a writer of Roman times, as a Cretan sweet.

1 kg roughly chopped walnuts
½ cup sugar, ½ cup ground toasted bread
2 tbsp ground cinnamon and clove
½ kg commercial pastry
3/4 cup olive oil for basting the pastry sheets
❖ ***Syrup:*** **1 cup honey, ½ cup sugar**
3/4 cup water, 2 tbsp lemon juice

In a large bowl mix walnuts, toasted bread, sugar, cinnamon and clove powder. Brush a rectangular oven tray with olive oil and place 4 pastry sheets, one at a time, brushing each one with olive oil. Spread about 1/3 of the nut mixture over the last sheet and place 2 pastry sheets over the nuts, one at a time, brushing again with olive oil. Continue in this manner till all the ingredients are used up. On top, place 4 pastry sheets, each one brushed with olive oil. Sprinkle the top sheet with a little water and olive oil. Cut into serving portions with a sharp knife, first vertically and then horizontally. Bake in preheated oven (180° C.) till golden brown. In the meantime prepare the syrup: In a large saucepan put sugar, honey, water and lemon juice and bring to a boil. Simmer for 5-6 minutes and pour hot syrup over hot baklavas, as soon as you remove it from oven.

Yoghurt cake with olive oil

½ cup olive oil, 1 cup sugar
5 eggs, 250 grams yoghurt
3 teaspoons baking powder
1 teaspoon grated lemon rind
2½ cups flour

Beat olive oil with sugar and continue by adding yolks, lemon rind, yoghurt, flour sifted with baking powder and finally egg whites beaten stiff. Combine very carefully and transfer the mixture into an oiled No 30 baking tin. Bake in preheated oven (180° C) for about 50 minutes.

Raisin cake with olive oil

1½ cups olive oil, 1½ cups sugar
2 cups fresh orange juice, 2 teaspoons baking soda
1 cup liquid from boiled cinnamon or water
50 ml brandy, 2 teaspoons baking powder
1 tbsp ground cinnamon and clove

1 cup seedless raisins, 1 teaspoon grated orange rind
½ cup coarsely ground walnuts (optional)
1 kg all purpose flour

In a large bowl start beating olive oil and sugar and then add boiled cinnamon, baking soda diluted in orange juice, baking powder diluted in brandy, cinnamon and clove powder, orange rind, walnuts, raisins and finally flour, working the mixture as you go along. Transfer the mixture into an oiled No 40 baking tin and bake in preheated oven (moderate heat) for 1 hour and 15 minutes.

Apple cake with olive oil

½ cup olive oil
1 cup sugar, 5 eggs
1 tbsp ground cinnamon and clove powder
1 teaspoon baking soda
juice of 1 lemon, 3 tbsp brandy
2 cups all-purpose flour, 2 teaspoons baking powder
1 kg apples, cut into thin slices
2 grated pears or 1 pear and 1 quince

Prepare the mixture: Beat olive oil with sugar, and continue with cinnamon and clove, egg yolks, baking soda diluted in lemon juice, baking powder diluted in brandy, flour and finally the egg whites beaten stiff. Combine carefully and pour half mixture in an oiled No 32 baking tin. Place fruit on top and pour the rest of the mixture on the fruit. Bake in moderate heat (preheated oven) for almost an hour.

Carrot cake with olive oil

½ cup olive oil, ½ cup sugar
1 tbsp ground cinnamon
1 teaspoon grated orange rind
3/4 cup fresh orange juice
½ cup grated carrot
½ cup grated apple
3/4 cup seedless raisins
½ cup coarsely ground walnuts
4 tbsp brandy
2 cups all purpose flour
2 teaspoons baking powder

Beat olive oil with sugar, add cinnamon powder, orange rind, orange juice, carrot, apple, raisins, brandy and finally flour mixed with baking powder. Combine well.
Brush a baking pan with olive oil, pour mixture into it and bake in preheated oven (180° C.) for about 50 minutes.

Walnut cake with olive oil

1 cup olive oil, 1 cup sugar
6 eggs, 1 cup milk
1 tbsp ground cinnamon and clove
1 cup coarsely ground walnuts
3 cups flour, 3 teaspoons baking powder
❖ ***Syrup***: 1 cup sugar, 1 tbsp honey
½ cup water, 1 tbsp lemon juice

In a large bowl start beating olive oil with sugar and add yolks, cinnamon and clove, walnuts, baking powder diluted in milk and the flour, stirring the mixture continuously. In the end add egg whites which have been beaten very well and combine very carefully. Pour the mixture in an oiled No 32 baking tin and bake in moderate heat for a little less than an hour. Remove the cake from oven and let it cool down a little. *Prepare the syrup:* Put sugar, honey, water and lemon juice in a pot and boil for 10 minutes. Pour hot syrup over warm walnut cake.

Olive oil cake

1,5 cup olive oil, 1,5 cup sugar
1 cup milk, 4 eggs
2 teaspoons baking powder
grated rind and juice of 1 lemon
1 teaspoon baking soda
1 tbsp ground cinnamon and clove
3,5 cups all-purpose flour

In a large bowl beat olive oil and sugar and continue by adding yolks, cinnamon and clove, lemon rind, baking soda diluted in lemon juice, baking powder diluted in milk, flour and finally egg whites beaten stiff. Combine the whites very carefully with the rest of the mixture, transfer in oiled No 32 baking pan and bake in preheated oven (moderate heat) for about 50 minutes.

Kourambiethes (sugar-coated biscuits) with olive oil

Kourambiethes are the traditional Christmas sweets all over Greece. They are sold in Greek cake shops on those days or can be found packaged in supermarkets. In any case, it is customary to prepare kourambiethes at Christmas in every Greek house.

2 cups olive oil, ½ cup sugar, 4 tbsp brandy
1 tbsp ground cinnamon, 1 whole egg and 1 yolk
1 cup almonds, roasted and coarsely ground
½ kg flour
2 cups icing sugar

In a large bowl beat olive oil and sugar thoroughly and continue with eggs, brandy, cinnamon, almonds and slowly flour until you have soft dough which does not stick to the hands. Take pieces of dough the size of a walnut and shape round, oblong or oval kourambiethes. Place on oiled baking pan or on cookie sheet and bake in moderate heat for 15-20 minutes. Remove from oven, let kourambiethes cool slightly and sift icing sugar over them until they are completely covered.

Raisin biscuits

1 cup olive oil, ½ cup sugar
1 teaspoon ground cinnamon
½ teaspoon ground clove
1 teaspoon grated orange rind
1 teaspoon baking soda
½ cup fresh orange juice
1 teaspoon baking powder, 3 tbsp brandy
½ cup almonds or walnuts, coarsely ground
1 cup seedless raisins (sultanas)
½ kg all-purpose flour

Dust raisins with a little flour and mash in food processor for 5 minutes. In a large bowl beat olive oil and sugar and continue with the rest of the ingredients. Finaly add flour until the dough becomes soft and smooth. Take pieces of dough the size of a walnut and shape round biscuits. Place on baking sheet and bake in moderate heat for 20 minutes or until they are golden brown.

Honey biscuits (Melomakarona)

Melomakarona, like kourambiethes, are traditional Christmas sweets.

2 cups olive oil
½ cup caster sugar, 2 tbsp honey
1 teaspoon baking soda, 1 teaspoon baking powder
2 cups fresh orange and tangerin juice

1 teaspoon grated orange rind
1 tbsp cinnamon and clove powder
½ cup coarsely ground walnuts (optional)
1 cup fine semolina
1200 grams all-purpose flour
❖ ***Syrup**:* 1 cup honey, 1 cup sugar, 2 cups water
1 cup roasted and ground sesame seeds or walnuts
1 teaspoon ground cinnamon

In a large bowl beat olive oil with sugar and honey. Add orange rind, cinnamon and clove, baking soda and baking powder diluted in fruit juice, walnuts and

semolina, beating all the while. Slowly add flour until the dough is soft and malleable. Cover and let the dough stand for 30 minutes before using. Take pieces of dough the size of a small egg and form rounded oblong melomakarona. Place on baking sheet and bake in moderate heat for about 20 minutes. While melomakarona are cooling, prepare the syrup.
Dip melomakarona in the syrup and allow them to soak up for 1 minute. Place on a serving tray and sprinkle with sesame seeds or walnuts and cinnamon.

Olive oil biscuits (Koulourakia)

3 cups olive oil
2 cups sugar
juice of 1 medium orange and 1 lemon
1 tbsp ground cinnamon
5 tbsp brandy
2 teaspoons baking powder
1 teaspoon baking soda
1 cup roasted sesame seeds
1200 grams all-purpose flour

In a large bowl beat olive oil and sugar until creamy. Add baking soda diluted in juice, cinnamon, baking powder diluted in brandy and sesame seeds, beating all the while. Slowly sift flour as much as needed until the dough is soft and elastic. Cover and put dough in refrigerator for 30 minutes.
Take pieces of dough the size of a small walnut and roll into a rope. Join the ends to form circles and place koulourakia on baking sheet. Bake in moderate heat for 20 minutes, until golden brown.

Orange biscuits

2 cups olive oil, 2 cups sugar
1 cup fresh orange juice
1 tbsp ground cinnamon and clove
1 tbsp baking powder, 1 teaspoon baking soda
1 kg all-purpose flour (more or less)

In a large bowl beat olive oil and sugar until creamy. Continue by adding cinnamon and clove, baking soda diluted in orange juice and finally flour sifted together with baking powder until the dough is soft and elastic and doesn't stick to the hands. Cover with a towel, refrigerate for half an hour and then shape the biscuits: Take pieces of dough the size of a walnut and roll into a rope. Join the ends to form circles and place koulourakia on cookie sheet. Bake in moderate heat for 20 minutes until golden brown.

Semolina pudding (Chalvas)

1 cup olive oil, 2 cups fine semolina
2,5 cups sugar, 4 cups water
½ cup seedless raisins (optional)
1 tbsp ground cinnamon
½ cup chopped walnuts or pine nuts

In a pot, over medium heat, bring sugar and water to a boil and simmer for 10 minutes. Remove from heat and add raisins. In a large pot heat olive oil until it begins to sizzle. Slowly add semolina, stirring constantly for about 10 minutes with a wooden spoon until semolina is lightly brown. Add walnuts and then the syrup very slowly stirring constantly and being careful not to burn yourself as the mixture will bubble. Stir over low heat for about 10 minutes, until the syrup is completely absorbed by the semolina. Remove from heat and pour chalvas in a large mold or in several small ones. Sprinkle with ground cinnamon and walnuts, if desired. (Instead of raisins you can add dried plums or crystallized fruit.

Raisin Bread

3 packets dry active yeast
½ cup olive oil, 1 cup sugar
½ cup fresh orange juice
1 cup seedless raisins
1 teaspoon ground cinnamon
½ teaspoon ground mastic
2 kg all-purpose flour

In a bowl dilute the yeast in 1 cup lukewarm water. Dust raisins with a little flour and put aside. In a large bowl sift together flour and sugar, make a well in the center and add diluted yeast, olive oil, orange juice, cinnamon, mastic and raisins. Stirring constantly, add lukewarm water (about 2 cups) until soft and elastic dough is formed. Cover and let it rise until double in size, about 1-2 hours. Divide into balls, the size you want and shape oblong loaves. Place in bread tins, cover with towel and allow them to rise again until double in size. Brush with milk or beaten egg and bake in moderate heat for 40-45 minutes, until golden brown.

Cheese pastries (kallitsounia) with olive oil

❖ ***For the pastry dough:*** 1 cup olive oil
1 cup sugar
5 eggs
2 tbsp grated orange or bergamot peel
1 cup milk
2 teaspoons baking powder
about 1300 grams flour

❖ ***For the filling:*** 1,5 kg myzithra cheese
½ cup sugar, 2 egg yolks
1 tbsp grated orange or bergamot peel
2 tbsp flour

Prepare the dough with the above ingredients, cover and leave aside to rest. Combine the myzithra with the rest of the ingredients for the filling. Take pieces of dough the size of a walnut and roll each one into a 10-12 cm circle.

Place 1 teaspoon of the filling on each circle and shape them into triangles or squares. You can also make small oil lamps ("lychnarakia") by pinching the edges together.

Place the "kallitsounia" on oiled baking tin, dab with beaten egg and bake in moderate heat for about 20 minutes, until golden brown.

Fried myzithra cheese with honey

6 slices of myzithra, 2 cm thick
½ cup flour
½ cup honey or grape juice syrup
½ cup chopped walnuts or hazel nuts
½ cup olive oil for frying

Heat olive oil in a pan, dredge myzithra slices with the flour and fry them until golden brown on both sides.

Transfer into a plate, pour honey or grape juice syrup over them and sprinkle with walnuts or hazel-nuts.

INDEX OF RECIPES

❖ **Dry measures:**

1 cup flour = 150 grams
1 cup semolina or caster sugar = 130 grams
1 cup sugar = 230 grams
1 cup rice = 230 grams
1 cup grated cheese = 100 grams
1 cup chopped almonds or walnuts = 100 grams

❖ **Liquids:**

1 cup = 225 ml
1 cup = 16 tablespoons (tbsps)
1 tablespoon = 3 teaspoons
1 tablespoon = 15 ml
1 teaspoon = 5 ml